...others

Sarah Tullett

Croner Publications Ltd
Croner House
London Road
Kingston upon Thames
Surrey KT2 6SR
Telephone: 0181-547 3333

Copyright © 1997 Croner Publications Ltd.

Published by
Croner Publications Ltd
Croner House
London Road
Kingston upon Thames
Surrey KT2 6SR.

While every care has been taken
in the writing and editing of this book,
readers should be aware that only Acts of Parliament
and Statutory Instruments have the force of law,
and that only the courts can authoritatively
interpret the law.

British Library Cataloguing in Publication Data
A CIP Catalogue Record for this book
is available from the British Library.

ISBN: 1 85524 424 1

Printed by
Whitstable Litho Ltd, Whitstable, Kent.

THE AUTHOR

SARAH TULLETT BSc, CBiol MIBiol, MIOSH, MRSH.

Sarah is Health and Safety Adviser to The Children's Trust, a charity which provides care, treatment and education for disabled children.

She is a founder member of the Health and Safety / Risk Management Contact Group, which has been set up as an informal forum for people with health and safety responsibility within charity organisations.

Sarah is also Editor of Croner's *Health and Safety at Work* loose leaf, a member of the Editorial Advisory Board for the *Health and Safety Briefing*, and a regular contributor to many other Croner manuals and news briefings.

REVIEWER

STEPHEN KING BSc (Eng), FIOSH, MIIRSM, FRSH, DipSM, RSP.

Stephen King is a Registered Safety Practitioner. He became a director of Personnel Health and Safety Consultants Ltd in 1990 after a career in health and safety management in the corporate sector.

He is a past Chairman of London Occupational Health, Safety and Hygiene Group and a former Secretary to the South East Branch of the Institution of Occupational Safety and Health (IOSH).

He is a contributor to Croner's *Health and Safety at Work*, the author of Croner's *Display Screen Equipment* and Consultant Editor of Croner's *Office Health and Safety*.

INTRODUCTION

Modern health and safety legislation is designed to offer everyone at work adequate protection from any identified hazards and associated risks, regardless of their age, gender, race, health status or condition, etc. However, there are still certain situations which may arise in a workplace that require more detailed and specialist attention. One such area is in the protection of new or expectant mothers, especially if they are known to be at particular risk.

As many of the adverse effects on pregnancy occur in the very early stages, perhaps before the woman is even aware she is pregnant, employers should determine and assess any activities which could put new or expectant mothers at risk, and ensure that there is advice and information readily available for women who are thinking of becoming pregnant. The aim of this book is to highlight and discuss a diverse variety of situations which employers may be required to address in relation to their work activities, and in relation to the activities of any new or expectant mothers in their employment.

Although the book is primarily geared towards health and safety issues, it has been necessary for the sake of completeness to include some associated peripheral areas such as employment law and general health awareness and/or promotion. Each chapter starts with a short introduction to the subjects covered and ends with a summary of the key points raised.

CONTENTS

QUESTIONS AND ANSWERS: NEW AND EXPECTANT MOTHERS

NEW AND EXPECTANT MOTHERS

Q1.   What does the term 'new and expectant mother' mean?

Q2.   Is there a legal definition of 'given birth'?

Q3.   What are the main effects of pregnancy?

Q4.   Why are these effects significant in a health and safety context?

Q5.   Why is health and safety significant in the post-natal period?

Q6.   Is there any time limit on the period of breast feeding?

RESPONSIBILITIES AND RIGHTS

Q7.   What are the principal duties of employers under the **Health and Safety at Work, etc Act 1974** with respect to new or expectant mothers?

Q8.   Do employers have additional responsibilities under other health and safety legislation?

Q9.   What other legislation is particularly relevant to new or expectant mothers?

Q10.   What are the main provisions of these pieces of legislation?

Q11.   What responsibilities do employees have for health and safety?

Q12.   Are there any specific legal duties on new or expectant mothers?

Q13.   Are new or expectant mothers who are self-employed given any legal protection against work-related risks to their health and safety?

Q14.   Are there any duties owed to foetuses and children?

Q15.   Do the risks to men of reproductive age have to be taken into consideration as well?

Q16.   Are there any relevant actions under civil law?

Q17. What are the civil actions available?

Q18. Is the employer's common law duty of care absolute?

Q19. Can compensation awards be reduced if the employee was found to have contributed to the negligence which caused the injury?

Q20. Is there a time period within which civil actions must be brought to court?

Q21. Are there any other means of seeking compensation?

Q22. Are employers obliged to give new or expectant mothers time off for associated medical checks, etc?

SPECIFIC HEALTH AND SAFETY ISSUES

Q23. Should new or expectant mothers be specifically addressed in the employer's health and safety policy?

Q24. Are there any specific requirements for risk assessments in relation to new or expectant mothers?

Q25. What is a risk assessment?

Q26. What are the main stages of a risk assessment?

Q27. What is the difference between 'hazard' and 'risk'?

Q28. Is the procedure the same for all risk assessments?

Q29. Can employers carry out generic risk assessments for all new or expectant mothers?

Q30. Do risk assessments have to be repeated under the **Management of Health and Safety at Work Regulations 1992**, if they are required by other legislation?

Q31. Do new or expectant mothers have any duties in relation to risk assessments?

Q32. What is the recognised hierarchy of control measures?

Q33. Are there any specific control measures employers are obliged to consider in relation to new or expectant mothers?

Q34. What are the specific controls that need to be considered in relation to new or expectant mothers?

Q35. What does 'suitable' alternative work mean?

Q36. Are there any conditions which must be met before the employer is obliged to take the specific control measures discussed above?

Q37. If the employer refuses to find alternative work or to suspend the new or expectant mother on full pay is there any course of redress?

Q38. What hazards are particularly relevant to new or expectant mothers?

Q39. What are physical agents?

Q40. Can physical agents harm an unborn child?

Q41. What are the general effects of physical agents on new or expectant mothers?

Q42. Is there a greater duty of care owed to women who have given birth by caesarean section?

Q43. What control measures should employers consider for women who have given birth by caesarean section?

Q44. What is whole body vibration and why is it significant to new or expectant mothers?

Q45. What controls should be considered to avoid or reduce the risks associated with whole body vibration?

Q46. Are pregnant women and nursing mothers at risk from manual handling activities?

Q47. What are the risks associated with manual handling activities to new or expectant mothers?

Q48. How can the risks associated with manual handling be identified?

Q49. What does a manual handling risk assessment involve?

Q50. Are new or expectant mothers at particular risk through using display screen equipment?

Q51. Are new or expectant mothers entitled to longer or more frequent breaks away from display screen work?

Q52. Are new or expectant mothers entitled to free eye sight tests if they perform display screen work?

Q53. Who exactly is a display screen equipment user?

Q54. Do employers have any duties to new or expectant mothers who use display screen equipment at home?

Q55. Are new or expectant mothers who are self-employed owed any duties in relation to display screen work?

Q56. Will display screen work which is set at a pre-determined rate cause a problem for new or expectant mothers?

Q57. Is radiation a significant display screen hazard and are new or expectant mothers particularly at risk?

Q58. What are biological agents?

Q59. Which biological agents are new or expectant mothers most at risk from?

Q60. Are there times when new or expectant mothers, foetuses or babies are more susceptible to the risks posed by biological agents?

Q61. What control measures can be taken to avoid or eliminate the risks associated with biological agents?

Q62. What about the risks of infection to new or expectant mothers through contact with the public?

Q63. Can new or expectant mothers be given vaccines?

Q64. What are chemical agents?

Q65. Which chemical agents are known to have an adverse effect on the foetus?

Q66. How is it possible to identify chemical agents which are hazardous to health?

Q67. Where can information on hazardous substances be found?

Q68. What are 'risk' and 'safety' phrases and which ones are relevant to new or expectant mothers?

Q69. What are teratogenic and mutagenic substances?

Q70. How do hazardous substances enter the body?

Q71. What measures are available for controlling exposure to chemical agents?

Q72. Are there any other hazardous chemical agents which are not covered by the COSHH Regulations?

4

Q73. What are the risks to new or expectant mothers associated with lead?

Q74. Is carbon monoxide hazardous to foetuses?

Q75. Are men of reproductive age at risk from chemical agents, and is there an associated risk to any offspring?

Q76. What are the effects of chemical agents on new or expectant mothers, foetuses or babies?

Q77. What are the risks to new or expectant mothers from radiation?

Q78. What are the main work environment concerns in relation to new or expectant mothers?

Q79. What are the main factors to be considered with regard to access and/or egress routes used by new or expectant mothers?

Q80. What happens if new or expectant mothers cannot use an emergency escape route safely?

Q81. Should a member of staff be nominated to assist new or expectant mothers during an evacuation?

Q82. Can new or expectant mothers be adversely affected by temperature extremes?

Q83. Should new or expectant mothers be provided with seating at work?

Q84. What factors need to be considered with respect to new or expectant mothers in relation to work space and workstations?

Q85. Is noise a significant hazard to new or expectant mothers?

Q86. Can smells generated by a work activity adversely affect new or expectant mothers?

Q87. Is there any requirement for employers to provide specific welfare facilities for new or expectant mothers?

Q88. Are there any other welfare factors which must be considered?

Q89. Can new or expectant mothers work shifts?

Q90. Do some shift patterns represent a greater risk than others?

Q91. Can new or expectant mothers work a normal length day?

Q92. Are new or expectant mothers entitled to additional breaks from their work?

Q93. Are new or expectant mothers at particular risk from operating machinery?

Q94. Are slips, trips and falls significant hazards to new or expectant mothers?

Q95. Are new or expectant mothers at greater risk from work-related stress than other employees?

Q96. Should new or expectant mothers be allowed to work in potentially violent situations?

Q97. Are there any restrictions on new or expectant mothers travelling?

Q98. Do pregnant women have to wear road vehicle safety belts?

Q99. Are there any special considerations for new or expectant mothers who have to work abroad?

Q100. Are there any special insurance provisions which apply to the employment of new or expectant mothers?

Q101. Are members of the public who are new or expectant mothers covered by any special insurance?

Q102. Are new or expectant mothers who work on a temporary or casual basis protected by health and safety law?

EMPLOYMENT ISSUES

Q103. What is the main legislation governing the employment rights of new or expectant mothers?

Q104. Can a pregnant woman work right up to her period of confinement?

Q105. If an employer requests medical confirmation that a pregnant woman is fit to continue working late into her pregnancy, can this be construed as sex discrimination?

Q106. What is the current period of maternity leave?

Q107. Do employers have to maintain the new or expectant mother's contractual rights for the whole period of her maternity leave?

Q108. Are there any qualifying periods of service or hours of work which must be satisfied by new or expectant mothers before they are entitled to maternity leave?

Q109. How much notice do new or expectant mothers have to give employers of the fact that they are pregnant and intend to go on maternity leave?

Q110. Are there any restrictions as to when maternity leave can start?

Q111. Can new mothers return to work immediately after the birth of their baby?

Q112. When does the maternity leave period end?

Q113. What notice period is a new mother required to give her employer of her intention to return to work?

Q114. What employment protection do new or expectant mothers have while they are pregnant or on maternity leave?

Q115. Are new mothers returning from maternity leave entitled to have their old jobs back?

Q116. Are employers obliged to give pregnant women time off for ante-natal care?

Q117. Is there any course of redress for new or expectant mothers whose employers do not fulfil their obligations?

Q118. Are employers obliged to provide nursery facilities or child care facilities?

GENERAL HEALTH ISSUES

Q119. What are the dangers of exposure to tobacco smoke on new or expectant mothers?

Q120. What effects do drugs and alcohol have on new or expectant mothers?

Q121. Can foetuses and babies contract the human immunodeficiency virus (HIV) from their mothers?

Q122. Can mothers pass allergies on to their babies?

Q123. Do employers have a right to request medical information which relates to any of their employees who are new or expectant mothers?

Q124. Can employers request new or expectant mothers to undergo a medical at any time in their employment?

Q125. Are new or expectant mothers allowed access to the report of any medical examination they are required to undergo at work?

Q126. What is the correct procedure for employers to follow if they require medical information about a new or expectant mother?

Q127. Is there any statutory requirement governing the issues of confidentiality?

Q128. Are there any times when confidentiality can be broken?

Q129. What examples are there of pre-existing health problems which may be significant in the case of new or expectant mothers?

NEW AND EXPECTANT MOTHERS

INTRODUCTION

Pregnancy is a dynamic condition leading to the eventual birth of a child. While pregnancy *per se* need not necessarily represent a specific risk with regard to health and safety, the pregnant female will undergo significant physiological, hormonal and psychological changes which may warrant closer attention. This is also true of the period of care after the birth. This chapter defines important terms and considers the various changes which occur during pregnancy and post-natal nursing.

Q1.   What does the term 'new and expectant mother' mean?

A.   This is basically a legal term used to describe pregnant women (expectant mothers) and women who have just given birth (new mothers). The origin is in the **Management of Health and Safety (Amendment) Regulations 1994** (SI 1994 No. 2865) which give a more detailed definition as follows:

> *"new or expectant mother means an employee who is pregnant; who has given birth within the previous six months; or who is breast feeding".*

Q2.   Is there a legal definition of 'given birth'?

A.   Yes. Again the definition appears in the **Management of Health and Safety (Amendment) Regulations 1994**, which state that 'given birth' means *"delivered a living child or, after 24 weeks of pregnancy, a stillborn child".*

Q3.   What are the main effects of pregnancy?

A.   It is important to clarify that pregnancy is not a disease and is not automatically debilitating — many women remain completely healthy and are able to work productively up until the start of their maternity leave and later while breast feeding.

Pregnancy is a dynamic, ie constantly changing, condition which causes physiological and psychological changes to occur in the female body. These effects are controlled by a sequence of hormonal changes throughout the pregnancy and the period afterwards. The degree and resultant effects of these changes are highly individual.

The most obvious change that occurs is the increase in girth size as the foetus (baby) develops inside its mother. There are also associated effects such as morning sickness, swollen ankles, varicose veins, haemorrhoids, increasing fatigue, backache, increased number of visits to the toilet and reduction in manual dexterity and mobility. Pregnancy can, amongst other things, also increase body blood volume and water retention, adversely affect the digestion of carbohydrates, eg sugars, etc leading in some cases to diabetes, and increase respiratory sensitivity to carbon dioxide leading to hyperventilation.

Q4. Why are these effects significant in a health and safety context?

A. The system of health and safety controls in place within the UK are generally accepted as offering all workers a safe level of protection from the hazards associated with their work. However, there are certain cases where additional protection may be required due to the increased susceptibility of an individual or group of people (see *Responsibilities and Rights* section below).

The various physiological, etc effects experienced by new and expectant mothers may make them particularly vulnerable at certain times. As such they may require additional control measures in order to ensure their health and safety and that of their child.

Q5. Why is health and safety significant in the post-natal period?

A. Once a baby has been born there are still many changes occurring in the mother as her body re-adjusts to the non-pregnant state — these may maintain her status as being at special risk and therefore warranting additional controls. Also, if the mother breast feeds there is a possibility of certain chemicals or biological agents, eg bacteria or other infections, being passed from the mother's milk to the feeding baby.

Q6. **Is there any time limit on the period of breast feeding?**

A. The relevant regulations, ie the **Management of Health and Safety at Work Regulations 1992** (SI 1992 No. 2051) and the **Management of Health and Safety at Work (Amendment) Regulations 1994** (SI 1994 No. 2865), *do not* specify a definite time limit for the period of breast feeding. Therefore, any appropriate controls must be continued for the entire period that the mother chooses to breast feed.

SUMMARY

Pregnancy and the post-natal period of nursing cause many physiological, hormonal and psychological changes to occur in the mother which may in turn represent significant health and safety risks in relation to her work. These particular risks must be suitably and appropriately addressed. There may also be some risks to the new or unborn child and again these must be adequately controlled.

RESPONSIBILITIES AND RIGHTS

INTRODUCTION

Under statute health and safety law, and civil law, certain specified individuals have defined duties to others. The extent of those duties varies according to the particular law in question. In addition to these imposed duties, some individuals have certain rights. In the context of health and safety, the responsibilities and rights relate to the duty to ensure any individual's health and safety from any work-associated risks, and the rights of redress if something does go wrong.

This chapter considers the main legal provisions and civil duties but does not aim to discuss the practical implications. These will be discussed in the following chapter *Specific Health and Safety Issues*.

Q7.   **What are the principal duties of employers under the Health and Safety at Work, etc Act 1974 with respect to new or expectant mothers?**

A.   **The Health and Safety at Work, etc Act 1974** (HSW Act) (ss. 2 and 3) imposes a specific duty on employers to ensure the health and safety of employees at work, and anyone else (non-employees) who may be adversely affected by the employer's work activities, so far as is reasonably practicable.

By implication this requires employers to recognise the hazards and risks associated with their work and to take the necessary preventive and protective measures to eliminate or adequately control them, ie carry out a risk assessment (see *Specific Health and Safety Issues* — risk assessments, section below). In fulfilling these duties, the employer must take into account any plant, equipment, substances or materials which new or expectant mothers use, handle or otherwise may come into contact with, the work environment, and the premises where the work is carried out.

The duty owed under the HSW Act is owed to employees individually not collectively. This means that a greater duty of care is owed to individuals who are more susceptible to the risks associated with their work than other employees. If new or expectant mothers are specifically at risk, then they are entitled to a greater level of protection — this applies whether they are employees or visitors to the employer's premises.

It should also be noted that the HSW Act includes the protection of mental as well as physical well being, and addresses health, safety and welfare issues.

Q8. **Do employers have additional responsibilities under other health and safety legislation?**

A. Many subordinate regulations do impose further duties on employers, the main ones are discussed below.

1. **Management of Health and Safety at Work Regulations 1992** (Management Regulations) (SI 1992 No. 2051).

   These regulations impose several requirements of importance to new or expectant mothers and form the basis of an effective health and safety management system within the workplace. The main requirement is for employers to carry out a risk assessment of the hazards and risks associated with their work undertaking.

   Risk assessments are discussed in more detail below but in summary they should identify the work-related hazards, evaluate the associated risks and determine the preventive and/or protective measures needed to eliminate or at least adequately control those risks. The risk assessment should also identify individuals or groups who are especially at risk from the work and who may require additional protection. This could include new or expectant mothers.

   Also of particular relevance is the requirement for employers to take into account the capabilities of individual employees to perform the intended task(s). In the case of new or expectant mothers this situation should be kept under review, as should the risk assessment, as the woman's capabilities will alter throughout the term of her pregnancy and period of post-natal nursing.

These regulations also require the employer to implement health and safety arrangements, appoint competent persons to assist in complying with the provisions, and carry out health surveillance where there is an identified risk to health and safety. Procedures must also be in place for dealing with emergency situations, for providing any necessary information and training to employees, and to any other person who may need that information in order to ensure their own health and safety, or that of other persons. There are also provisions for employers who share premises, or who utilise the employees of another employer, ie contractors, and who use temporary workers.

2.   The **Management of Health and Safety at Work (Amendment) Regulations 1994** (Amendment Regulations) (SI 1994 No. 2865).

These regulations specifically require employers to assess the risks to new or expectant mothers where they may be at greater risk from the work undertaking than non-pregnant, etc employees.

The regulations, in conjunction with the **Employment Rights Act 1996**, also define a hierarchy of acceptable control measures for employers to implement where there is an enhanced risk to new or expectant mothers. In summary, these control measures include altering working conditions and/or hours of work, finding suitable alternative work, and in some cases suspension from certain work activities (see *Specific Health and Safety Issues* section below).

The Management Regulations expressly prohibit breaches of those regulations being used in civil actions. However, the Amendment Regulations do allow new or expectant mothers to sue their employer through civil proceedings for a failure to undertake a suitable and sufficient risk assessment of the risks to them under the Management Regulations, where they have suffered an injury as a result of that failing.

Note: there are also relevant statutory provisions under a various parts of employment law legislation (see *Employment Issues* section below).

Q9. **What other legislation is particularly relevant to new or expectant mothers?**

A. As employees, new or expectant mothers are covered by any health and safety legislation that applies to their place of work and work activities. The legislation is designed to offer, as a minimum, adequate protection to all employees regardless of their age, gender or health status. However, in meeting these minimum standards, employers may have to adapt or adopt existing or new control measures in order to ensure vulnerable groups, such as new or expectant mothers, are adequately protected in practice.

The **Manual Handling Operations Regulations 1992**, the **Workplace (Health, Safety and Welfare) Regulations 1992**, the **Control of Substances Hazardous to Health Regulations 1994**, as amended, the **Personal Protective Equipment at Work Regulations 1992**, as amended, and the **Health and Safety (Display Screen Equipment) Regulations 1992** may have particular significance.

Q10. **What are the main provisions of these pieces of legislation?**

A. 1. The **Manual Handling Operations Regulations 1992** (SI 1992 No 2793) require employers to avoid all manual handling activities, ie lifting, carrying, or supporting, etc, any load by bodily force, where there is a risk of injury, so far as is reasonably practicable. If such manual handling activities cannot be avoided then the activities must be assessed and the associated risks reduced to the lowest level reasonably practicable.

The significance of these regulations to new or expectant mothers is that such a woman (and an unborn child) will become increasingly vulnerable to injury arising from manual handling activities during the term of her pregnancy and during the maternity period after the birth. The assessment of risk in these cases must be kept under regular review so that any changes in the woman's ability to lift, etc safely are known and acted upon.

2. The **Workplace (Health, Safety and Welfare) Regulations 1992** (SI 1992 No 3004) lay down provisions that are related to the work environment and welfare facilities. Specific areas that are addressed include: maintenance, ventilation, temperature, lighting, cleanliness and refuse, work space, workstations, seating, floors and traffic routes, protection against falls and falling objects, windows, glazing, doors, gates, escalators and moving walkways, and the provision of toilet, washing, changing, rest, and drinking water facilities.

    Two particular points of note. First there is a specific duty on employers to provide suitable rest facilities for pregnant women or nursing mothers, and second employers are obliged to protect non-smokers from the effects of tobacco smoke in rest areas — this may be particularly significant during the first few weeks of a woman's pregnancy. The significance of these regulations to new or expectant mothers is that the work environment in which such women are required to work may have implications for their health and safety during the term of their pregnancy and post-natal period.

3. The **Control of Substances Hazardous to Health Regulations 1994** (COSHH) (SI 1994 No 3246) as amended require an assessment to be made of all exposures to substances that cause, or may cause, any adverse health effects — this includes chemical substances, biological agents, substantial quantities of dust, and any other substances if these are capable of causing adverse health effects. COSHH specifically defines the term 'hazardous substances' and requires all such exposures to be prevented or at least adequately con-

trolled. In addition, COSHH also requires the proper use of any control measures implemented, and their maintenance, examination and testing, the monitoring of workplace exposures, the provision of health surveillance in defined circumstances and the provision of information, instruction and training for persons exposed to hazardous substances.

The exposure limits to certain chemicals are detailed in the COSHH Regulations and in accompanying guidance. Exposure limits are published annually in HSE document EH40, and are generally set at levels that are safe for all employees, however there are a few cases where lower levels are set for new or expectant mothers than for other workers. Although covered by their own specific legislation, ie the **Control of Lead at Work Regulations 1980** (SI 1980 No. 1248) and the **Ionising Radiations Regulations 1985** (SI 1985 No. 1333), and not by COSHH, lead and ionising radiations are hazardous substances which may adversely affect new or expectant mothers or their foetuses or babies.

The significance of all these regulations to new or expectant mothers is the known adverse effect many chemicals, biological agents and other harmful substances can have on the mother, foetus or breast feeding child.

4.   The **Personal Protective Equipment at Work Regulations 1992** (SI 1992 No 2966) require employers to provide suitable personal protective equipment (PPE) in situations where any identified risks cannot be controlled by other means. An assessment must be carried out to determine whether the PPE is suitable for the intended use and the wearer. It must be compatible with other PPE required to be used, well-maintained, and properly stored in designated accommodation. Employers must inform, instruct and train employees in the use of the PPE and the hazards it is designed to control. Damaged or lost PPE must be reported and replaced.

The significance of these regulations to new or expectant mothers is that some of the physiological changes which occur during pregnancy and the period of breast feeding may affect the ability of such women to wear PPE correctly and comfortably, and may therefore reduce the level of protection the PPE is designed to offer.

5. The **Health and Safety (Display Screen Equipment) Regulations 1992** (SI 1992 No 2792) require that the workstations of display screen users and operators are assessed and meet the minimum requirements set out in the Schedule to the regulations. The provision of breaks away from display screen work, eye sight tests, information and training are also covered.

    The significance of these regulations to new or expectant mothers is the suitability of the workstation, which should be assessed throughout the term of pregnancy to account for the physiological changes, and the requirement for regular breaks or changes of activity.

Q11. What responsibilities do employees have for health and safety?

A. Section 7 of the **Health and Safety at Work Act 1974** (HSW Act) requires employees to take reasonable steps to ensure their own health and safety at work and to ensure that they do not put anyone else at risk through their activities whilst at work. In relation to new or expectant mothers this means that they have a duty to protect themselves and their foetus or child who may be adversely affected by the mother's work. Work colleagues also have a duty to ensure that they do not harm a new or expectant mother or her foetus or child — this duty includes injuries or harm caused by 'fooling around'.

    Section 7 also requires employees to co-operate with the employer in order for all relevant statutory provisions, ie legal duties, to be complied with. This means employees have a duty to follow procedures and practices implemented by the employer to protect their health and safety. There should be full and proper consultation with employees before the introduction of new procedures or practices into the workplace.

Many of the subordinate regulations also impose specific duties on employees, such as using work equipment, etc in accordance with any training, information or instruction given — this would apply equally to new or expectant mothers.

Q12. **Are there any specific legal duties on new or expectant mothers?**

A. Yes. Section 7 of the **Health and Safety at Work Act 1974** (HSW Act) requires employees to safeguard their own health and safety, and that of others who may be affected by their work. New or expectant mothers therefore have a duty to themselves, and also to ensure the health and safety of their unborn or breast fed child. In addition, employers are only obliged to fulfil some of their duties under the **Management of Health and Safety at Work (Amendment) Regulations 1994** and the **Employment Rights Act 1996** when the new or expectant mother has notified them of her condition, and/or if necessary, produced a signed medical certificate, ie new or expectant mothers have a duty to notify their employer of their condition before the employer is obliged to take any specific control measures.

The relevant provisions of the Amendment Regulations are the requirements on the employer, in relation to new or expectant mothers, to: alter her working conditions and/or hours of work; provide suitable alternative work; or ultimately suspend her, including on medical advice, suspension from night work, where the risks to her health and safety cannot be adequately controlled by existing preventative or protective measures.

In all these cases, employers are only required to act when they have been given written notification by a woman that she is pregnant or nursing a baby. In addition, the employer is only obliged to maintain the above arrangements if the new or expectant mother has produced, on request and within a reasonable time, a certificate signed by a medical practitioner or registered midwife confirming she is pregnant.

Various employment law-related provisions such as allowing paid time off for ante-natal care must also be addressed by employers once the new or expectant mother has notified them that she is pregnant.

Q13. **Are new or expectant mothers who are self-employed given any legal protection against work-related risks to their health and safety?**

A.   Section 3 of the **Health and Safety at Work Act 1974** (HSW Act) requires self-employed persons to ensure their own health and safety at work and to ensure that they do not endanger anyone else. New or expectant mothers who are self-employed will need to take appropriate control measures to protect themselves and their unborn child or baby. In practice, it is likely that much self-employed work will be office-based and therefore generally low risk, although workstations and posture may be areas of concern. The benefits are that much more flexible work arrangements are possible, which allows the new or expectant mother to adapt her work according to her particular needs at any one time.

The **Health and Safety (Display Screen Equipment) Regulations 1992** (SI 1992 No. 2792) require employers who provide display screen equipment workstations to operators, ie self-employed persons, to assess those workstations and ensure they meet the minimum requirements laid down.

Q14. **Are there any duties owed to foetuses and children?**

A.   Yes. The **Congenital Disabilities (Civil Liability) Act 1976** (1976 Act) provides for civil liability in cases where children have been born disabled due to the fault of some person. Where children are born disabled as the result of an occurrence which adversely affected the ability of either parent to have normal children, or which adversely affected the mother during the pregnancy, then the disability is regarded as damage resulting from the act or omission of the person responsible.

If an employer had been found negligent or in breach of a statutory duty that directly resulted in the employee giving birth to a disabled child, then the employer will be liable under the 1976 Act. Any damages awarded against the employer in such cases will be reduced by a proportional amount if it can be proven that the employee(s) shared the responsibility of the child being born disabled. The employer will not be answerable to the child where the wrongful act, etc occurred before conception and the parent(s) were aware of the risks.

Q15. **Do the risks to men of reproductive age have to be taken into consideration as well?**

A. Yes. In situations where there is a potential genetic or reproductive risk which could adversely affect foetuses or children, ie in work involving ionising radiation or certain chemicals, etc, then the employer also has a duty to consider the risks of such work activities to men of reproductive age as well as to women (regardless of whether these women are new or expectant mothers).

Q16. **Are there any relevant actions under civil law?**

A. Yes. Employees who have sustained a personal injury as a result of their work may use the civil courts to seek compensation against their employer. Civil actions may be based on breach of statutory duty and/or negligence.

Note: some legislation expressly prohibits breaches of their provisions being used in civil proceedings, eg ss. 2–8 of the **Health and Safety at Work Act 1974** (HSW Act) and the **Management of Health and Safety at Work Regulations 1992** (SI 1992 No. 2051). The **Employers' Liability (Compulsory Insurance) Act 1969** requires employers to take out liability insurance before they may legally operate any business.

The purpose of the insurance is to cover any compensation claims awarded against employers in the civil courts for personal injury sustained by employees during the course of their employment. If employees are killed in the course of their employment, their dependants may also seek compensation.

Q17. **What are the civil actions available?**

A. There are two common courses of action available through the civil courts, ie breach of a statutory duty or negligence. These are briefly discussed below.

1. Breach of a statutory duty

   Employees may bring a civil claim if the employer has breached a statutory duty. It should be noted that not all breaches of statutory duty may be pursued through the civil courts, indeed some Acts and regulations expressly prohibit breaches of their provisions being used in civil proceedings, eg ss. 2–8 of the **Health and Safety at Work Act 1974** (HSW Act) and the **Management of Health and Safety at Work Regulations 1992** (SI 1992 No. 2051) (Management Regulations).

   Note: this exclusion under the Management Regulations does not apply to the risk assessment required to be carried out on the risks to new or expectant mothers under the 1994 Regulations.

   For a civil claim to be upheld for breach of a statutory duty employees must prove:
   – they were covered by the statutory provisions
   – that the injury sustained was of a kind the statutory duty was aimed at preventing
   – that the employer was in breach of this duty
   – that the breach of duty caused the injury.

2. Negligence

   Besides any statutory duties, employers also owe a personal duty of care under common law, ie non-statutory law, to their employees, and it is the breach of this duty of care that forms the basis of negligence. In cases of negligence, it is usually the employee who has to prove that the employer was negligent. Nowadays most compensation cases are based on negligence which is recognised as consisting of the following three elements:

- a general duty of care to prevent foreseeable injuries
- that duty is broken if someone acts in a negligent manner
- the breach of that duty must result in the injury or damage.

Again the duty is owed to employees individually, not collectively, so a greater duty of care may be owed to new or expectant mothers.

Generally employers only owe a duty of care to their own employees, although there are some circumstances where this is extended to the employees of others. In fulfilling the duty of care, employers should consider the safety of the plant, appliances and premises, the systems of work, and the other employees.

Q18. **Is the employer's common law duty of care absolute?**

A. The standard of care owed to employees is not absolute, ie the employer does not have to guarantee complete absence of injury. However, the standard of care is that which any reasonable employer may be expected to owe in the light of current knowledge, etc. Employers cannot be liable for anything they could not be expected to be aware of, or could not foresee, although once the risk has been perceived then preventive steps must be implemented.

Q19. **Can compensation awards be reduced if the employee was found to have contributed to the negligence which caused the injury?**

A. Yes. Employees who caused, or partially caused, their own injury may be held to be contributorily negligent and any compensation awarded may be reduced accordingly. Contributory negligence of 100%, ie the injury was deemed to be entirely the fault of the employee, is possible but rare. Contributory negligence may also involve other employees if they are partly to blame for an injury occurring.

Q20. **Is there a time period within which civil actions must be brought to court?**

A. Actions taken for personal injury must be initiated within three years of the accident, or in situations where there is a lag period between the harmful exposure and the injury, etc, then within three years of the first awareness /diagnosis of the injury. Courts may permit actions outside the limitation period in some cases. In the case of minors, ie persons under the age of 18 years, there is no time limit for bringing a civil action, however, once the minor has attained the age of 18 years the three year time limit will apply, ie they have until they are 21 years old to bring a civil case.

Q21. **Are there any other means of seeking compensation?**

A. Yes. Apart from civil court action, the two other common ways for injured employees to claim compensation are through the National Insurance Industrial Injuries scheme, which allows them to qualify for certain benefits if their injuries render them incapable of work, or through the Prescribed Industrial Injuries legislation. These schemes, as with civil actions, are open to all workers who sustain an injury at work, and are not specific to new or expectant mothers.

1. National insurance industrial injuries scheme

   In the first instance, employers will pay statutory sick pay (SSP) at the prescribed rate for the first 28 weeks of any period of sickness absence. Employees injured at work and eligible for SSP will receive the SSP from the employer for this period. Injured employees who are not eligible for SSP, or who have exhausted their SSP allowance, may claim one of the following state benefits:

   - *incapacity benefit* which is payable at three different rates depending on the period of incapacity, for a specified time and for which there are no contribution conditions when claimed in relation to an industrial injury, although a medical test is included

- *disablement benefit* which is payable where employees are assessed to have suffered a 14% or more loss of mental or physical faculty.

Industrial death benefits have now been abolished, although widows of industrial deaths may be entitled to claim national widow's benefits.

The accident causing the injury must have:

- occurred during the course of employment, including situations where the employee was injured doing something expressly prohibited by the employer or by specific legal provisions
- been such that the injury would have occurred anyway
- been such that the employee's actions were for the purpose of the employer's work and within the scope of the employee's job.

Benefits are also payable where employees are injured going to the assistance of other employees or trying to avert an accident, and where they are injured by the misconduct of another person, or by the presence of an animal or bird, etc, providing the employee was in the course of employment and did not contribute to the occurrence of the accident.

2.   Prescribed industrial injuries

The **Social Security (Industrial Injuries) (Prescribed Diseases) Regulations 1985** (SI 1985 No. 967), as variously amended, list prescribed diseases and conditions, which, if they occur under the corresponding prescribed occupations will qualify employees to receive the benefits described above. Generally the employee is required to have been in that occupation for a minimum period, ie usually one month (10 years for occupational deafness). The four categories of prescribed diseases or injuries are:

- conditions due to physical agents
- conditions due to biological agents

> - conditions due to chemical agents
> - miscellaneous conditions.

These lists of prescribed diseases are periodically updated by amending regulations.

Q22. **Are employers obliged to give new or expectant mothers time off for associated medical checks, etc?**

A.   Under health and safety law there is no specific requirement for a new or expectant mother to be automatically allowed time off for medical check ups, etc in relation to her pregnancy or post-natal period, *unless* there is an identified risk to her health and safety that is directly associated with the work activity she is/was performing. In these cases, employers are obliged to implement health surveillance routines which may necessitate the need for medical examinations in work time, without any detriment to the woman's terms and conditions of employment.

Under the **Employment Rights Act 1996** there is a statutory right for pregnant women to take time off for ante-natal care purposes (see *Employment Issues* — time off — ante-natal care, section below).

SUMMARY

New and expectant mothers are owed both statutory and common law duties of care to ensure their health and safety, by their employer. This duty extends to ensuring that the foetus or breast feeding child does not suffer any adverse effects to their health and safety as a result of the new or expectant mother's work.

Children who are born with disabilities which can be directly linked to the negligence of some person, have the right of redress against the person who was negligent. In situations where the foetus may be harmed through the exposure of the potential father to a hazard known to have genetic or reproductive effects, then the employer is obliged to eliminate or at least adequately control those risks.

Compensation for a new or expectant mother who suffers personal injury or ill-health as a result of her work is available through the civil courts for breach of statutory duty or negligence. They may also seek compensation through the National Insurance Industrial Injuries scheme, or through the social security prescribed Industrial Injuries legislative system for which various state benefits are available.

SPECIFIC HEALTH AND SAFETY ISSUES

INTRODUCTION

The previous chapter considered the main responsibilities to, and of, new or expectant mothers under both statute and common law. This chapter expands on those duties by discussing some of the practical health and safety issues employers may have to address in respect of new or expectant mothers.

Q23. **Should new or expectant mothers be specifically addressed in the employer's health and safety policy?**

A.   There is no specific requirement for new or expectant mothers to be addressed in the employer's health and safety policy statement. However, if there are identified risks to them associated with the work undertaking it would be sensible to have a procedure for dealing with that situation, including any relevant notifications, so that new or expectant mothers are aware of any risks and the appropriate control measures, and know what is required of them.

Q24. **Are there any specific requirements for risk assessments in relation to new or expectant mothers?**

A.   Yes. The **Management of Health and Safety at Work (Amendment) Regulations 1994** (SI 1994 No. 2865) specifically require employers to extend the risk assessment under the **Management of Health and Safety at Work Regulations 1992** (Management Regulations)(SI 1992 No. 2051) to include new or expectant mothers where their condition puts them at particular risk from their work.

The need to undertake a risk assessment is also implied under ss. 2 and 3 of the **Health and Safety at Work Act 1974** (HSW Act), ie the duties on employers to ensure the health and safety of employees and non-employees, so far as is reasonably practicable. In addition, there are also specific requirements for a risk assessment to be carried out under the **Manual Handling Operations Regulations 1992** (SI 1992 No. 2793), the **Control of Substances**

Hazardous to Health Regulations 1994 (SI 1994 No. 3246), and the **Health and Safety (Display Screen Equipment) Regulations 1992** (SI 1992 No. 2792). The need for a risk assessment is implied in the **Workplace (Health, Safety and Welfare) Regulations 1992** (SI 1992 No. 3004) and the **Personal Protective Equipment at Work Regulations 1992** (SI 1992 No. 2966). In all of these latter cases, the need for risk assessment applies generally for all workers and is not specific for new or expectant mothers.

Where new or expectant mothers work at home on the employer's business, then the risk assessment must include any hazards and risks associated with the work in that environment. Training, information and instruction on the hazards identified and the necessary controls will be very important in these situations.

Q25.   What is a risk assessment?

A.   A risk assessment requires employers to identify the hazards, evaluate the risks and determine the necessary control measures associated with each of the following factors:

- every work activity including routine work and non-routine work such as maintenance, emergency responses to call outs, etc
- every material, article or substance, used or produced at work, including waste items
- every item of work equipment
- every workplace, workstation and working environment.

The risk assessment should also identify exactly who is at risk from each hazard, especially potentially vulnerable groups such as new or expectant mothers, and include consideration of all the work procedures in place at the time of the assessment. The purpose of risk assessment is to determine and implement measures that will prevent, or at least protect against, the hazards identified.

Q26.   What are the main stages of a risk assessment?

1.   Hazard identification

Hazard identification is simply an acknowledgement of everything that has the potential to cause harm and the people that are likely to be affected. Trivial hazards may be ignored so that the emphasis is on the control of significant hazards that could result in a serious injury and/or that could affect a lot of people.

2. Risk evaluation

    Once the hazards have been identified, the risks associated with each hazard must be evaluated. This may be carried out in a number of ways, although it is important to take into account the likelihood of exposure to the hazard and the severity of the outcome, in the risk evaluation. It is also important to take into account any existing control measures that are in place and their current effectiveness and efficiency. There is a requirement to record 'significant findings' where employers employ five or more employees, except where the assessment can be easily and quickly repeated.

3. Determination of control measures

    The final stage in, and the purpose of, a risk assessment is to determine the effectiveness of existing control measures and whether any additional measures are necessary to eliminate or at least reduce the risk to an acceptable level. Control measures may include training programmes for staff, the display of warning signs to indicate a hazard, the use of local exhaust ventilation to remove dusts and fumes or, as a last resort, the use of personal protective equipment or clothing.

Q27. What is the difference between 'hazard' and 'risk'?

A. It is important to appreciate the subtle difference between the terms 'hazard' and 'risk'. Hazard is the potential something has to cause harm, while risk is the realisation of that harm actually occurring in relation to how likely it is to occur, and the severity of the outcome if it does.

Q28. Is the procedure the same for all risk assessments?

A. Essentially yes. The methodology will be the same for all risk assessments regardless of whom the control measures aim to protect. The differences will be in evaluating the risks of certain hazards to particular individuals, eg new or expectant mothers, especially if those individuals are at increased risk, and in determining the control measures necessary to ensure their health and safety. Account must obviously be taken of any statutory requirements or legally defined exposure limits, eg the **Ionising Radiations Regulations 1985** (SI 1985 No. 1333) define exposure levels of radiation in relation to pregnant women, and the **Control of Lead at Work Regulations 1980** (SI 1980 No. 1248) define the levels of lead in blood for women of reproductive capacity. The **Control of Substances Hazardous to Health Regulations 1994** (COSHH) (SI 1994 No. 3246) define exposure levels for various chemicals, although not in relation to new or expectant mothers specifically.

Q29. **Can employers carry out generic risk assessments for all new or expectant mothers?**

A. No. Although in some cases it will be appropriate for employers to carry out generic risk assessments, ie one assessment that applies to similar work activities in similar workplaces; it is worth reiterating that the duty of care, both in statute and common law, is owed to employees as individuals. This may mean 'fine tuning' a generic assessment so that the risks to particularly vulnerable individuals are eliminated or at least adequately controlled. Where the risk evaluations and necessary control measures are different for new or expectant mothers compared to the other employees collectively, these must also addressed.

Q30. **Do risk assessments have to be repeated under the Management of Health and Safety at Work Regulations 1992, if they are required by other legislation?**

A. No. Where risk assessments are also required under legislation other than the **Management of Health and Safety at Work Regulations 1992** (Management Regulations) (SI 1992 No. 2051), there is no need to repeat these if they remain valid to the current circumstances and adequately assess and address the risks to new or expectant mothers. Generally, compliance with the more specific legislative requirements, eg the **Control of Substances**

Hazardous to Health Regulations 1994 (COSHH) (SI 1994 No. 3246), will be sufficient to ensure compliance under the Management Regulations, as amended.

Where risks to new or expectant mothers have been identified, employers must ensure that all women of child bearing age and capacity are informed of those hazards and the necessary control measures. In some work situations, ie work involving exposure to ionising radiation and certain chemicals, it may also be necessary to inform male employees of the reproductive risks.

Q31. Do new or expectant mothers have any duties in relation to risk assessments?

There are no specific duties on new or expectant mothers in relation to risk assessments over and above those they have as employees, ie to safeguard their own health and safety and that of others who may be affected by their work (including the foetus or baby), and to co-operate with their employer in complying with relevant legislation. However, as employers do have a duty to address the risks to new or expectant mothers associated with their work undertaking, it follows that the new or expectant mother would be well-advised to notify the employer of her condition in order that additional control measures can be implemented if necessary. Some formal notification procedure may be considered necessary.

Q32. What is the recognised hierarchy of control measures?

A. There is a recognised control hierarchy which states that where possible, hazards should be:
- prevented or eliminated
- substituted for less hazardous substances, machinery or processes, etc
- enclosed or otherwise isolated
- adequately controlled, preferably by engineering controls
- exposed for the shortest time
- made to effect the least number of people
- controlled by personal protective equipment as a last resort.

In many cases the standard of what is acceptable as a risk is arbitrary and will depend on a number of factors particular to each organisation, and to each individual employee, although there may well be some official guidance on specific risks. The standards of control achieved by individual organisations will also depend on the objectives set in their health and safety policy and the effectiveness of implementing, and monitoring the actual performance against those objectives.

Q33. **Are there any specific control measures employers are obliged to consider in relation to new or expectant mothers?**

A.   Yes. The **Management of Health and Safety at Work (Amendment) Regulations 1994** (SI 1994 No. 2865) and the **Employment Rights Act 1996** require employers to follow a sequence of actions to ensure the health and safety of new or expectant mothers, where the risks to them cannot be avoided or adequately controlled by the means required under other legislation.

Q34. **What are the specific controls that need to be considered in relation to new or expectant mothers?**

A.   Under the **Management of Health and Safety at Work (Amendment) Regulations 1994** (SI 1994 No. 2865) (Amendment Regulations), the employer must, where it is reasonable to do so, alter the working conditions or hours of work of new or expectant mothers if doing so would avoid the risks associated with their work. If these measures are not reasonable or would not avoid the risks identified, then s. 67 of the **Employment Rights Act 1996** requires suitable alternative work to be offered.

In situations where suitable alternative work is not available, the Amendment Regulations further require employers to suspend the new or expectant mother for as long as is necessary to avoid the risks. The suspension can be extended to night work if the employer receives a signed certificate from a registered medical practitioner or midwife stating that such a suspension is necessary in the interests of the woman's health and safety.

Q35.   What does 'suitable' alternative work mean?

A.   Section 67 of the **Employment Rights Act 1996** states that in order for alternative work to be considered suitable it must be suitable for a new or expectant mother to perform and appropriate for her condition. Additionally it must not cause any detriment in her terms and conditions of employment.

In practice 'suitable' has to be considered from both a health and safety and an employment law perspective. As the reason for offering alternative work on health and safety grounds is to avoid exposure to workplace risks which cannot be adequately controlled by other means, then the alternative work must not represent similar or increased risks, or create any new ones, in relation to a new or expectant mother, ie it must be safer and/or healthier for her than her former work.

From an employment law point of view 'suitable' takes into account the job status, place of work including travelling, pay, hours of work and other terms and conditions of employment.

It is worth noting that alternative work which is 'suitable' will usually be 'appropriate' as well, although there may be times where this is not so and both individual factors will have to be addressed. For example, the alternative work may be healthier, safer, and equal with regards to terms and conditions of employment, etc, ie it is suitable, but it may not be able to accommodate scheduled absences necessary for ante-natal, or child care purposes, etc, ie it is not appropriate for the new or expectant mother's condition.

Q36.   Are there any conditions which must be met before the employer is obliged to take the specific control measures discussed above?

A.   Yes. Employers are not obliged to alter working conditions, hours of work, find suitable alternative work, or suspend a new or expectant mother until they have received a written notification from the woman confirming that she is either pregnant, or has given birth within the last six months, or is breast feeding.

Where the suspension relates to night work the new or expectant mother must provide her employer with a signed certificate from a registered medical practitioner or registered midwife stating that such a suspension is necessary for her health and safety.

The employer is also exempted from maintaining any of the actions detailed above, including the suspension from night work where the woman has not provided written notification of her condition, or has failed to produce a certificate signed by a registered medical practitioner or midwife, within a reasonable time of being requested to do so by the employer. This exemption also applies where the employer knows the woman is no longer pregnant or cannot establish whether she remains so.

Q37. **If the employer refuses to find alternative work or to suspend the new or expectant mother on full pay is there any course of redress?**

A.   Yes. The **Employment Rights Act 1996** provides that if employers do not fulfil their obligations to the required standard, then the new or expectant mother is entitled to take her case to an Industrial Tribunal. It is generally accepted that unpaid benefits should also still be provided to new or expectant mothers suspended from work for health and safety reasons. However, if suitable alternative work has been unreasonably refused by the new or expectant mother then she forfeits the right to paid remuneration during her suspension.

Q38. **What hazards are particularly relevant to new or expectant mothers?**

A.   The specific risks to consider in respect to new or expectant mothers are defined in Annexes I and II of the Pregnant Workers' Directive (92/85/EEC) and fall into one of three categories, ie physical agents, biological agents and chemical agents. Relevant aspects of working conditions which may adversely affect new or expectant mothers are also discussed. Details are given in the Health and Safety Executive's (HSE) publication HS(G) 122 *New and expectant mothers at work — a guide for employers*, which is available from HSE Books, see page 87.

When considering the hazards that work activities, etc represent to new or expectant mother, it is important to take into account the physiological, psychological and hormonal effects of the pregnancy and the post-natal period afterwards.

Q39. What are physical agents?

A. Physical agents are recognised as including shock; low frequency, particularly whole body, vibration; excessive movement; manual handling activities; noise; ionising and non-ionising radiation; temperature extremes; postures and movements that cause mental and/or physical fatigue; and hyperbaric (high pressure) atmospheres.

The effects of physical agents vary between pregnant women and nursing mothers, although nursing mothers are more likely to be protected by the controls implemented for the workforce as a whole, without any special adjustments being necessary. The exception is exposure to ionising radiation which may contaminate a breast fed baby if the mother's skin becomes contaminated.

Q40. Can physical agents harm an unborn child?

A. Ionising radiation and work in hyperbaric atmospheres (high atmospheric pressure work) are the only physical agents known to directly affect the unborn foetus and there are consequently strict exposure controls laid down in the associated legislation on pregnant women working in these fields. Exposure to whole body vibration may cause the placenta to become detached from the womb.

Q41. What are the general effects of physical agents on new or expectant mothers?

A. The effects of physical hazards include increased tiredness and fatigue; increased chance of miscarriages, due to actions such as whole body vibration which may cause a detachment of the placenta from the womb, and an increased risk of premature births and lower birth weights. In the case of babies with lower birth weights, maternal fatigue at work, and/or repetitive boring work are suggested as being influencing, if not causative factors.

Q42.   Is there a greater duty of care owed to women who have given birth by caesarean section?

A.   Yes. If an employee is particularly susceptible to any risks associated with their work, for what ever reason, then their employer owes them a greater duty of care. This includes women who have returned to work after a caesarean section who will consequently have restricted capabilities, for example such women will have limited mobility, a significantly reduced ability to perform manual handling activities, etc, and they may find many working postures awkward and/or uncomfortable, particularly if they are required to stay in one position for long periods of time.

Q43.   What control measures should employers consider for women who have given birth by caesarean section?

A.   The primary control in these situations is to avoid, or at the very least reduce to an acceptable level, exposure to the specific risk being considered. In some situations the provision of seating, an adjustment to working hours, including longer and more frequent breaks, the ability to move around and frequently change posture, and more direct control over the actual work will be considered appropriate controls. Manual handling activities and work which involves stretching, turning or bending, should be avoided until the woman is passed medically fit to perform such activities safely.

Q44.   What is whole body vibration and why is it significant to new or expectant mothers?

A.   Whole body vibration is caused by the body being in contact with a vibrating surface which transmits the vibration energy through the contact point to the body, ie the vibrating surface causes the whole body to vibrate. Parts of the human body vibrate at different frequencies and if the vibration source happens to vibrate at the same frequency as a particular part of the body then the vibration effect can be significantly amplified. Generally, organs suspended in the body have a higher natural frequency than structural parts.

The significance to new or expectant mothers is that low vibration frequencies of between 4 to 8 Hertz (Hz) are equivalent to the natural frequency of the abdominal mass which means the abdomen will be particularly susceptible in this frequency range. This could affect the womb and there is evidence that whole body vibration can cause the placenta to become detached from the womb wall. Premature babies and low birth weights have also been linked with exposure to whole body vibration.

Shocks and jolts to the abdomen may cause similar effects. Vibration frequencies of around 1 Hz can precipitate motion sickness and women in the early stages of pregnancy who are suffering from morning sickness may be subject to increased incidents of nausea and/or vomiting. There is no evidence that whole body vibration adversely affects women who are breast feeding.

Q45. What controls should be considered to avoid or reduce the risks associated with whole body vibration?

A.   As in all cases it is far better to avoid the risk altogether, so pregnant women should be taken off of work involving exposure to whole body vibration. Where the work cannot be avoided then suitable and effective damping measures should be implemented to reduce the level of vibration affecting the body, these may include specially designed standing mats, suspended vehicle seats, etc. Reduction in the length of time of exposure should also be considered.

Q46. Are pregnant women and nursing mothers at risk from manual handling activities?

A.   Yes. Manual handling activities pose a well recognised risk to new or expectant mothers.

Q47. What are the risks associated with manual handling activities to new or expectant mothers?

A. The most obvious factor is the increasing girth size of a pregnant woman during the latter part of the pregnancy, which will seriously hinder her ability to lift or move loads safely. In particular, it will be difficult for such women to hold loads securely, or in the best position, and they will be restricted in certain movements, eg bending, turning, stretching, etc. Hormonal changes during pregnancy affect the ligaments of joints which in turn can lead to a greater susceptibility to injury where stresses and strains occur as a result of a manual handling activity. Increased fatigue will also be a factor in a new or expectant mother's ability to perform manual handling activities safely.

Nursing mothers may be suffering from sore nipples and breasts, especially if they are breast feeding their babies, and will find it uncomfortable to hold loads close against their chests. The Health and Safety Executive's (HSE) guidance on manual handling L23 *Manual handling: guidance on the Manual Handling Operations Regulations 1992*, acknowledges that new mothers are also at particular risk from manual handling activities, especially in the three months after childbirth. This will be relevant to new mothers who underwent a caesarean section, in which case the increased level of risk may continue for a considerable period of time, ie until the operation wounds have properly healed, etc.

Q48. How can the risks associated with manual handling be identified?

A. The **Manual Handling Operations Regulations 1992** (SI 1992 No. 2793) require manual handling activities which have any risk of injury to be avoided, so far as is reasonably practicable. If the activity cannot be avoided then it must be assessed and the risk reduced to the lowest level reasonably practicable. In practice this is achieved by carrying out a manual handling risk assessment which should identify the associated hazards, evaluate the risks and determine the necessary control measures.

Q49. **What does a manual handling risk assessment involve?**

A.   Manual handling risk assessments should consider four factors, ie the load, the task, the environment and the individual's ability to perform the required manual handling activity.

   1.   The load

   This part should determine:

   – the weight of the load

   – whether the load is large/bulky/unwieldy

   – whether the load is difficult to grasp or hold securely

   – whether the weight is liable to move

   – whether the load is flexible or rigid

   – whether there are any inherent hazardous features such as extreme temperatures, sharp and/or rough edges, etc.

   The features of particular significance to new or expectant mothers are the weight and physical size of the load, and whether it can be held securely by her. Work situations in which the new or expectant mother is involved in caring for people or animals may subject her to instances where the load weight can suddenly shift or where the body goes rigid or floppy — all these factors will affect a new or expectant mother's ability to perform these manual handling activities safely. There is also evidence which suggests that heavy lifting could increase the risk of spontaneous abortion.

   2.   The task

   This part should determine:

   – whether the load is held away from the body

   – whether the activity involves any bending, stretching, twisting or stooping

   – whether the activity is repetitive

   – frequency and duration of recovery breaks away from the manual handling work

   – whether large vertical movements are necessary

   – whether strenuous effort is necessary, eg for pushing or pulling the load

    – whether the work rate is set at a predetermined level

    – whether the load has to be lifted or moved over long distances.

In this case the features likely to be of most significance to new or expectant mothers will be the posture that such women need to adopt in order to perform the task, eg bending, stooping, stretching, etc. The duration of the activity, the physical effort involved, the frequency and length of recovery periods, and the distances the load has to be lifted or moved over will also be significant, especially in later pregnancy when the pregnant woman becomes increasingly tired as a result of being less mobile.

3.   The environment

This part should identify:

    – whether there are constraints on posture, ie confined working spaces

    – poorly maintained access/egress routes, uneven floor surfaces

    – changes in floor level, eg stairs

    – any areas which are poorly lit, especially stairs

    – extreme temperatures and humidity within the workplace

    – the presence of strong air movements

    – high/annoying levels of noise.

In this case the features likely to be most significant to new or expectant mothers are constraints in working space which lead to poor posture, changes in floor level which may not be obvious in late pregnancy. Temperature extremes are also known to adversely affect pregnant women.

4.   The individual's ability

This part should determine:

    – whether an individual has any predisposing medical or other condition which puts them at increased risk from manual handling activities — this includes pregnancy and maternity period (note that an employee is obliged to inform the employer of any health condition that may make them more susceptible to injury — this would include pregnancy)

- whether individuals have a special need for training, information, instruction or supervision, if English is not the first language of the employee
- whether the manual handling activity requires any special capabilities.

The features likely to be most significant to new or expectant mothers are the pregnancy and maternity periods which will alter a new or expectant mother's ability to perform manual handling activities safely, and the requirement for 'special capabilities' which may exclude new or expectant mothers.

Q50. Are new or expectant mothers at particular risk through using display screen equipment?

A. There is no evidence that new or expectant mothers are at any greater risk than other employees who use display screen equipment. However, an employee who believes that she, or her unborn child, is at risk will be subject to mental stress, and reassurance/information should be provided. Employers should also take into account the physical changes which occur during pregnancy which may make the operating posture awkward and/or uncomfortable. Prolonged periods in one position may result in undue stresses and strains on a pregnant woman. In situations where the display screen work is intensive and over longer periods it may be necessary to move a woman in late pregnancy to alternative work. Fatigue and a reduction in the ability to concentrate during pregnancy and the post-natal period may also be relevant factors for consideration.

Q51. Are new or expectant mothers entitled to longer or more frequent breaks away from display screen work?

A. There is no provision in the **Health and Safety (Display Screen equipment) Regulations 1992** (SI 1992 No. 2792) which requires employers to allow longer or more frequent breaks to new or expectant mothers. However, if there is any risk to the health and safety of such women arising from display screen work, and the provision of appropriate breaks or changes of work activity is an acceptable control measure, then the employer is obliged to consider that course of action. In these situations, however, the provision of longer or more frequent breaks are as a result of the pregnancy and not of performing display screen work *per se*.

Q52. **Are new or expectant mothers entitled to free eye sight tests if they perform display screen work?**

A. Yes. Under the **Health and Safety (Display Screen Equipment) Regulations 1992** (SI 1992 No. 2792) employers are obliged to provide free eye sight tests to display screen equipment users, either on request of existing users, or when employees are about to become display screen users. This is a general duty to all display screen users and does not relate specifically to new or expectant mothers. Such eye sight tests must be made available at regular intervals while the user remains a display screen user. Completely separate to the requirement for the provision of eye sight tests under these Regulations, new or expectant mothers are also entitled to free eye sight tests as part of their social security benefits.

Q53. **Who exactly is a display screen equipment user?**

A. The simplest answer is someone who uses display screen equipment for a significant part of their normal work, and for the purpose of the employer's undertaking. By inference, if the display screen equipment is used for a significant part of the normal work, there may well be postural implications in relation to users who are new or expectant mothers which the employer will need to address.

Q54. **Do employers have any duties to new or expectant mothers who use display screen equipment at home?**

A. Yes. If an employee is required to use display screen equipment at home as part of their normal work, and that equipment is provided by the employer for the purpose of the employer's business, then such women are included in the definition of 'user' and are covered by all the provisions in the **Health and Safety (Display Screen Equipment) Regulations 1992** (SI 1992 No. 2792) which apply to users.

Such homeworking may be beneficial to new or expectant mothers who will be able to adopt a more flexible work routine to suit their particular needs. However, as the onus is on the new or expectant mother to ensure her own well being there is perhaps a greater duty on the employer to ensure such women are adequately and appropriately informed and trained in any associated risks and control measures.

The employer is also obliged to ensure any workstations used at home meet the minimum requirements laid down in the Regulations. In the case of pregnant women, the workstation may need to be assessed regularly during the term of pregnancy in order to ensure that the woman is not put at additional risk due to the physiological, etc changes which occur during the pregnancy.

Q55. **Are new or expectant mothers who are self-employed owed any duties in relation to display screen work?**

A.   Yes. Under the **Health and Safety (Display Screen Equipment) Regulations 1992** (SI 1992 No. 2792) employers have duties to display screen operators as well as to display screen users. Display screen operators are defined in the regulations as self-employed persons who use display screen equipment for a significant part of their normal work. The duties to assess workstations, ensure such workstations meet the minimum requirements (if the workstations are provided by the employer for the operator's use), and the provision of health and safety related information, including information on associated risks and necessary control measures, all apply to display screen operators. The provisions relating to breaks away from display screen work, training and eye sight tests do not apply to display screen operators.

Q56. **Will display screen work which is set at a pre-determined rate cause a problem for new or expectant mothers?**

A.   There is no reason to suspect that new or expectant mothers are at increased risk when performing display screen work which is set at a pre-determined rate. However, it should be borne in mind that pregnancy may cause a reduction in concentration and manual dexterity, and an increase in tiredness and the number of visits made to the toilet. Where any of these cause stress or distress to the new or expectant mother because she cannot keep up with the required rate, the employer may need to consider reducing the rate of the work to one suitable for the woman, or consider alternative work.

Q57. **Is radiation a significant display screen hazard and are new or expectant mothers particularly at risk?**

A.   Despite continual concern about the levels of electromagnetic radiation emissions from display screens there is no scientific evidence that there is an associated risk to health. Electromagnetic radiation levels which have been monitored are negligible and well below levels known to cause a risk to health.

There is no evidence that new or expectant mothers are at particular risk from any electromagnetic radiation emissions from display screens, or that there is any link between such emissions and increased incidences of miscarriages or birth defects.

However, employers may have to address situations where the new or expectant mother is very concerned about such emissions, even when the negligible level of risk is made clear. If the concern is causing stress and related symptoms in a new or expectant mother it may be necessary to find alternative work as a precautionary step.

Q58. **What are biological agents?**

A.   Biological agents include micro-organisms such as bacteria, viruses, human endoparasites (parasites which live inside the human body) and any other micro-organisms capable of causing infection, allergy, toxicity, or any other human health hazard. People most at risk from biological agents are those who work in specific work-places such as laboratories, human health and animal care serv-ices, agriculture, etc. The risk to new or expectant mothers from biological agents is not generally considered to be any different to that of other employees.

Q59. **Which biological agents are new or expectant mothers most at risk from?**

A.   The organisms of particular relevance to pregnant women are those known to cause adverse human health effects, especially abortion or physical/neurological damage to the foetus. The organ-isms may cause infection by transmission through the placenta, through breast feeding or through close maternal contact. The most relevant biological agents across all work activities, include hepa-titis B, human immunodeficiency virus (HIV) (the AIDS virus), tuberculosis (TB), syphilis, Rubella (German measles), Listeria and toxoplasma.

Q60. **Are there times when new or expectant mothers, foetuses or babies are more susceptible to the risks posed by biological agents?**

A.   New or expectant mothers are not generally considered to be at any greater risk from biological agents than other workers. How-ever, there are well-known risks to the foetus if the mother is exposed to, or contracts, certain infections during the pregnancy and maternity period. One of the main problems for employers is that the period of particular susceptibility of the foetus is often in the first 12 weeks of the pregnancy, when the mother may not be aware that she is pregnant or has not yet told her employer of her condition.

Employers are not obliged to control risks that they are not aware of, although it follows that if the workforce consists of women within the reproductive age range then control measures should be such as to offer adequate protection to women who could be, or who become, pregnant.

Babies may contract certain infections through their mother's milk.

Q61. What control measures can be taken to avoid or eliminate the risks associated with biological agents?

A.   The risk assessment should take account of the biological agent involved, how it is spread, and how likely an infection is. Depending on the official classification of the organism, there are detailed control measures laid down in the **Control of Substances Hazardous to Health Regulations 1994** (COSHH) (SI 1994 No. 3246), which may include avoiding exposure, containment of the work, high standards of personal hygiene (and proper provisions for ensuring this, eg showers), and the use of vaccines — provided that these do not increase the risk to the mother, foetus or child.

Q62. What about the risks of infection to new or expectant mothers through contact with the public?

A.   Generally, common infections within a community do not pose any special risk to new or expectant mothers over and above those to the community itself. There are certain situations, however, where there may be a known increase in risk, eg contact with Rubella (German measles) during the first 12 weeks of pregnancy. Women who work in contact with children, eg at a creche or school, may be at a greater risk.

Exposure to community infections are unlikely to be a significant work-related factor and is much more likely to be associated with travel to and from work, shopping, and other communal activities, etc. Employers may need to consider this if a new or expectant mother is required to travel on public transport systems, or mix with members of the public, as part of her work activities. If there is thought to be a significant risk to a new or expectant mother in individual cases, alternative work may need to be considered.

Q63. Can new or expectant mothers be given vaccines?

A.   It is generally accepted that vaccines of dead or attenuated viruses are safe to give to pregnant women, although the use of 'live' vaccines should be avoided, as should vaccines for rubella, mumps and measles. It may also be possible for some vaccines to pass into the mothers milk and into breast fed babies, and employers would be prudent to seek medical advice, either from the woman's general practitioner (with her written consent), or from the Health and Safety Executive's Employment Medical Advisory Service, before offering any vaccine to a new or expectant mother.

Q64. What are chemical agents?

A.   Chemical agents are chemical substances or preparations many of which are known to, or are suspected to, cause adverse effects to new or expectant mothers, foetuses and/or babies. The actual risk will be determined by the nature of the chemical, the route and degree of exposure, and other conditions at any particular work-place.

Q65. Which chemical agents are known to have an adverse effect on the foetus?

A.   Chemical agents such as mercury, lead, substances absorbed through the skin, cytotoxic drugs, carbon monoxide and chemicals labelled with the following risk phrases:

(a) possible risk of irreversible effects

(b) may cause cancer

(c) may cause heritable genetic damage

(d) may cause harm to the unborn child

(e) possible risk of harm to unborn child

(f) may cause harm to breast fed babies.

These are all examples of some chemical agents capable of adversely affecting the foetus. Generally speaking any substance covered by COSHH will need to be assessed and any specific risks to new or expectant mothers addressed.

Q66. **How is it possible to identify chemical agents which are hazardous to health?**

A.   Under the **Chemicals (Hazard Information and Packaging for Supply) Regulations 1994** (CHIP) (SI 1994 No. 3247) all chemicals which are classified as hazardous to human health must display a label on the container and also be accompanied by a safety data sheet. Vehicles which carry hazardous substances must also be appropriately and correctly labelled.

Q67. **Where can information on hazardous substances be found?**

A.   A lot of information on a hazardous substance may be obtained from the container label and the associated safety data sheet. All hazardous substances must be labelled and be covered by a safety data sheet.

The information of relevance on the label includes an indication of the danger and the appropriate hazard warning symbol, the associated 'risk' and 'safety' phrases, the name of the substance, the name, address and telephone number of the supplier, and other relevant information depending on the substance.

The safety data sheet should contain the following relevant information: substance identification; composition; first-aid measures; fire fighting measures; spillage/release containment; handling and storage information; exposure controls and personal protection; physical and chemical properties; reactivity and stability; toxicological and ecological information; waste disposal; transportation controls, and other relevant information. Safety data sheets must be revised in the light of any changes.

Q68. **What are 'risk' and 'safety' phrases and which ones are relevant to new or expectant mothers?**

A.   'Risk' and 'safety' phrases are pieces of information required to be included on the labels of hazardous chemicals, which give an indication of the associated risks (risk phrases) and the associated safety measures which should be taken (safety phrases). The risk phrases particularly relevant to new or expectant mothers are:

– R40: Possible risk of irreversible effects
– R45: May cause cancer
– R46: May cause heritable genetic damage
– R61: May cause harm to the unborn child
– R63: Possible risk of harm to the unborn child
– R64: May cause harm to breast fed babies.

Two or more risk phrases may be used together in 'combination risk phrases'.

All the other risk phrases will of course be relevant to all workers, including new or expectant mothers. Safety phrases provide information which is relevant to all workers and are not applicable to new or expectant mothers in particular.

Examples of safety phrases are:
– S2: Keep out of reach of children
– S8: Keep container tightly closed
– S37: Wear suitable gloves
– S51: Use only in well ventilated areas.

Two or more safety phrases may be used together in 'combination safety phrases'.

Q69. What are teratogenic and mutagenic substances?

A. Teratogenic substances are substances which cause deformities or other adverse effects in the foetus. Mutagenic substances are substances which are capable of causing changes in genetic material, eg chromosomes or genes, etc, which may in turn lead to deformities or other disabilities in any offspring. Women of child-bearing age and pregnant women are obviously at risk from exposure to these substances, men of reproductive age may also be at risk from these chemicals.

Q70. How do hazardous substances enter the body?

A. Chemicals can enter the body in three ways, ie inhalation, ingestion or through skin absorption. Of these routes, exposure through inhalation is the most common; ingestion of hazardous substances in a work context is rare. Once in the mother's body the chemicals may cross the placenta to the foetus or be passed on in breast milk which may affect babies who are breast fed.

The assessment of any substance which is hazardous to health, as required by the **Control of Substances Hazardous to Health Regulations 1994** (COSHH) (SI 1994 No. 3246), should take into account the likely route of any such exposures, as this will be significant in determining appropriate control measures.

Q71. **What measures are available for controlling exposure to chemical agents?**

A. Control measures include preventing exposure by total enclo-sure/isolation of the hazardous process, or substitution of a haz-ardous substance for a less hazardous one; effective engineering controls such as efficient extraction systems; good standards of personal hygiene; and as a last resort, the provision of suitable and appropriate personal protective equipment (PPE). If the work with chemical agents poses an unacceptable risk to new or expectant mothers, then suitable alternative work may need to be considered.

Unlike biological agents, there are a lot of legislative controls on the use and exposure to chemicals at work and in many cases there are associated exposure limits which must be adhered to. One important point to consider is that some chemicals may accumulate in the body and not show any adverse effects for some time; this may have serious implications for pregnant women, or women who are breast feeding.

Q72. **Are there any other hazardous chemical agents which are not covered by the COSHH Regulations?**

A. In addition to substances covered by the **Control of Substances Hazardous to Health Regulations 1994** (COSHH) (SI 1994 No. 3246) there are specific pieces of legislation covering lead, asbes-tos, and pesticides which define the necessary standards required for the safe use/exposure to that particular substance.

Q73. **What are the risks to new or expectant mothers associated with lead?**

A. Lead is one of the substances known to be able to enter the mother's milk and be passed on to breast fed babies. The nervous system of babies and young children is known to be especially sensitive to the effects of lead. Therefore any exposure of new or expectant mothers to lead should be avoided, or at the very least strictly controlled. The **Control of Lead at Work Regulations 1980** (SI 1980 No. 1248) contain provisions for the control of exposure to lead at work, including health surveillance where applicable. The accompanying approved code of practice (ACOP) lays down exposure limits for lead and defines the maximum permissible blood levels of lead for women of reproductive capacity. This lower level is designed to offer adequate protection against exposure in the early weeks of pregnancy before the woman may know she is pregnant.

Where pregnant women are subject to health surveillance under these regulations they will usually be suspended from any work which involves a significant exposure to lead. The dangers associated with exposure to lead and the effects on unborn children and babies have been recognised for many years and resulted in several pieces of factory-related legislation which prohibit the employment of women or young persons in certain processes involving lead. This older legislation is still in effect, although it is now gradually being replaced with modern legislation which is designed to offer adequate protection to all workers.

Q74. **Is carbon monoxide hazardous to foetuses?**

A. Yes. There is significant evidence that maternal exposure to carbon monoxide causes oxygen starvation in the foetus as carbon monoxide is able to pass readily across the placenta. Carbon monoxide interferes with the transportation of oxygen in the blood. There is no similar evidence that breast fed babies are at increased risk from maternal exposure to carbon monoxide.

Q75. **Are men of reproductive age at risk from chemical agents, and is there an associated risk to any offspring?**

A.   Yes. Certain chemicals are known to affect a man's ability to have 'normal', healthy children. The effects of such exposures usually affect sperm production, causing a reduction in the number of sperm, a reduction in the sperm mobility, or a complete absence of sperm production. Libido and potency changes may also occur as a result of exposure to some chemicals and this could ultimately affect conception. There will be a risk to any potential offspring if the exposure is to a mutagen, ie a substance capable of adversely affecting the genetic material which the father could pass on to any offspring.

Q76. **What are the effects of chemical agents on new or expectant mothers, foetuses or babies?**

A.   Chemical agents may affect women at the pre-conception, pregnancy and post-natal stages of reproduction. Alterations to menstrual cycle patterns may indicate an effect on the sex hormones, while other chemical agents may cause 'true' infertility by adversely affecting the egg in some way, or by preventing the egg attaching to the womb.

Chemical agents may also affect the foetus directly, or from the indirect effect of the chemicals on the mother. Common effects of exposure of foetuses to hazardous chemicals are termination of the pregnancy by abortion or miscarriage, stillborn babies, neonatal death or malformation, usually due to exposure to teratogenic or mutagenic substances.

Babies may become exposed to certain hazardous substances through drinking their mother's milk which has become contaminated through maternal exposure to the chemical in question. Most structural deformities are noticeable at birth or soon afterwards, although growth retardation, behavioural changes and the possibility of cancer may develop sometime afterwards.

Summary of possible fertility and foetal effects from exposure to chemicals

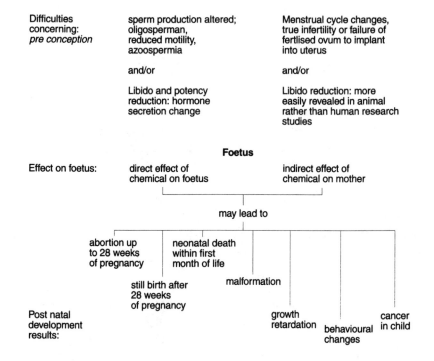

Difficulties concerning: *pre conception*	sperm production altered; oligosperman, reduced motility, azoospermia	Menstrual cycle changes, true infertility or failure of fertlised ovum to implant into uterus
	and/or	and/or
	Libido and potency reduction: hormone secretion change	Libido reduction: more easily revealed in animal rather than human research studies

Foetus

Effect on foetus: direct effect of chemical on foetus — indirect effect of chemical on mother

may lead to

abortion up to 28 weeks of pregnancy | neonatal death within first month of life

still birth after 28 weeks of pregnancy | malformation

Post natal development results: | growth retardation | behavioural changes | cancer in child

Q77. What are the risks to new or expectant mothers from radiation?

A. The risks associated with radiation depend on the type of radiation in question, ie ionising radiation or non-ionising radiation.

Ionising radiation, ie radioactive materials, are known to have teratogenic (cause deformities) and/or mutagenic (cause alterations to the genetic material) effects on a foetus. The exposure may be direct to the foetus or indirect through exposure of both or either parents at a pre-conception stage. Exposure to ionising radiation is strictly controlled by the **Ionising Radiations Regulations 1985** (SI 1985 No. 1333) which lay down detailed control measures including exposure limits.

The specific effects of exposure to non-ionising radiation, ie ultra violet (UV) light, infra red radiation, microwaves, electromagnetic fields, etc are less well-known in relation to new or expectant mothers. There are well-known effects on exposure to this type of radiation to people generally, ie prolonged exposure to UV light is linked with an increased risk of skin cancer. There have also been reports of higher incident rates of childhood leukaemia in areas of high exposure to electromagnetic fields — although this has not yet been scientifically proven.

There is certainly no evidence that level of emissions of non-ionising (electromagnetic) radiation from display screen equipment (VDUs) are harmful to new or expectant mothers. However, employers may have to address situations where the new or expectant mother is very concerned about such emissions, even when the negligible level of risk is made clear. If the concern is causing stress and related symptoms in a new or expectant mother, it may be necessary to find alternative work as a precautionary step.

It is not conclusively known whether new or expectant mothers, foetuses or new born babies are at particular risk from non- ionising radiation. Further information may be obtained from the Health and Safety Executive's Employment Medical Advisory Service (EMAS) who are located at the regional offices of the HSE or the National Radiological Protection Board (NRPB) (for contact details see *Useful Information* — addresses section below).

Q78. What are the main work environment concerns in relation to new or expectant mothers?

A.   New or expectant mothers may be particularly vulnerable to unsuitable and/or uncomfortable work environments. The main areas of concern are access and egress routes, emergency procedures and routes, temperature, seating, work space — including design and layout, and welfare facilities, such as toilets and rest areas, etc.

Q79. What are the main factors to be considered with regard to access and/or egress routes used by new or expectant mothers?

A.   Most access and egress routes to and from a place of work should not present any particular problems to new or expectant mothers. there may be reason for an employer to undertake a more detailed assessment if such routes are physically strenuous, as may occur in some older or listed multi-storied buildings with limited lift facilities, or if the routes, etc require a certain amount of agility, eg access, etc via ladders or scaffolding, or entry into vehicle driving cabs. In all of these situations the effects of pregnancy and maternity, such as increasing tiredness, increasing girth size and a reduction in mobility, agility and dexterity may have a significant effect in a new or expectant mother's ability to get to and from their place of work. If there is a significant risk to the new or expectant mother it may be necessary to consider relocation to a more accessible workplace.

Q80. What happens if new or expectant mothers cannot use an emergency escape route safely?

A.   This may again be more relevant to older and/or listed buildings, particularly those with narrow, metal external fire escapes. New buildings with spiral stair ways may also be a consideration if new or expectant mothers cannot leave the building quickly and safely.

The points to consider are:

-   can the new or expectant mother reach the escape route easily? If access to the route is through a designated window it may be difficult for a heavily pregnant woman to actually get to the escape route
-   is the evacuation of other persons likely to be hindered by a new or expectant mother to such an extent that those other persons are at risk?
-   once on the escape route, are there any parts which may present problems either to a new or expectant mother or any other person, that could affect their ability to evacuate? Such problem

areas may be vertical ladders attached to the building walls, steep spiral stairs, confined or, restricted spaces

- the amount of physical effort and general agility required
- the reason for the evacuation, ie evacuation for bomb threats may warrant different procedures than evacuation for fire.

In all cases planning is very important so that preventive action can be taken to avoid the problem occurring in the first place. This means that where a new or expectant mother cannot evacuate a building safely, or where her evacuation puts other people at risk, employers may have to consider temporarily relocating the new or expectant mother to a more readily evacuated area, ie from top floor to ground floor.

Q81. Should a member of staff be nominated to assist new or expectant mothers during an evacuation?

A. There is no obligation on employees, etc to assist new or expectant mothers (or anyone else) in an evacuation, especially if they put themselves at risk as a result of their assistance. Employers cannot impose this duty on an employee. The onus is on the employer to ensure that new or expectant mothers are not at risk through their work, and this includes ensuring they can evacuate the workplace safely. However, it would be prudent to notify fire marshals, etc of the presence of a pregnant woman/nursing mother, so that they can make a point of checking on her evacuation status in an emergency.

Q82. Can new or expectant mothers be adversely affected by temperature extremes?

A. The Approved Code of Practice which accompanies the **Workplace (Health, Safety and Welfare) Regulations 1992** (SI 1992 No. 3004) suggests that a reasonable working temperature, as required by the Regulations, is 16°C for non-strenuous work, and 13°C for strenuous work. Temperatures around these figures should not pose any particular problems to new or expectant mothers, although thermal comfort ranges are highly personal and may need to be addressed in individual cases. For work with display screen equipment, BS 7179 advocates a temperature of 19–23°C.

However, work in hot environments is known to cause haemorrhoids in some new or expectant mothers and employers should take appropriate control measures if this particular problem is brought to their attention. Work activities where this may need to be addressed include kitchens, laundries, hairdressers, etc.

There is also evidence of a slight increase in the risk of miscarriage for pregnant women who work in environments which are hot enough to raise their core body temperature.

Q83. **Should new or expectant mothers be provided with seating at work?**

A.   The **Workplace (Health, Safety and Welfare) Regulations 1992** (SI 1992 No. 3004) require employers to provide seating for employees who may perform their work satisfactorily sitting down. Any such seating so provided must be suitable for the person using it and for the type of work required to be performed. Footrests must also be provided if necessary, ie where the user cannot place their feet on the ground or where a correct seating posture cannot be attained with the seat alone. The seating should also provide support for the lower back.

The point to emphasise here is that the seating must be suitable for the user, so employers may have to consider different seating for new or expectant mothers where the existing seating is unsuitable for them. 'Suitable' is not defined, but the points to consider are general comfort — especially in later pregnancy, adequate support for the lower back, adjustibility, and ease of getting on or off, eg a high stool may be difficult for a pregnant woman to get on to and may give the impression that it is not stable if her balance, etc is affected. The available surrounding space is also important.

Non-specific backaches and varicose veins may result from prolonged periods of standing, and there is some suggestion that this is also associated with an increased risk of spontaneous abortion. However, prolonged periods of sitting may also cause problems so it is important for a new or expectant mother to be able to move around and change position regularly.

Q84. What factors need to be considered with respect to new or expectant mothers in relation to work space and workstations?

A.   The most obvious factor is the increasing size of a pregnant woman during the pregnancy which in many cases will necessitate the pregnant woman having to sit or stand further away from her work. This in turn may result in various postural problems causing backache and general fatigue if the body is having to continually stretch or lean. The increase in size may also restrict pregnant women working in small, awkward, confined spaces.

The actual layout of a workplace is also important so that people can move around freely and without coming into contact with pieces of protruding furniture, etc. In the case of pregnant women the layout may have to be adjusted to allow more room on passageways and through routes. Filing cabinets and drawer units should not open onto passageways in case they represent a trip hazard — this applies equally to all employees or any one else who may use the passageway, although in the later stages of pregnancy the increase in girth size may obstruct the view of items at floor level or just above. Balance and co-ordination may also be affected so a pregnant woman may not be able to save herself if she does trip or fall.

Q85. Is noise a significant hazard to new or expectant mothers?

A.   New or expectant mothers are as much at risk from excessive noise levels as any other worker, and the control measures of prevention, isolation, enclosure, ear protection, etc all apply. The regulations which govern exposure to noise at work are the **Noise at Work Regulations 1989** (SI 1989 No. 1790).

Q86. **Can smells generated by a work activity adversely affect new or expectant mothers?**

A.   The effect of smells on any particular individual is highly personal, depending on that person's olfactory sensitivity. Employers should prevent the formation and dispersion of smells around the workplace wherever possible, or at the very least take measures to protect the persons likely to be affected — especially where the presence of any smell is causing obvious discomfort or other adverse health effects (eg it is caused by a hazardous substance).

Generally new or expectant mothers should not be affected to a greater extent than anyone else by smells, although morning sickness may be induced or made worse by exposure to nauseating smells during the early stages of pregnancy.

Q87. **Is there any requirement for employers to provide specific welfare facilities for new or expectant mothers?**

A.   Yes. The **Workplace (Health, Safety and Welfare) Regulations 1992** (SI 1992 No. 3004) require employers to provide suitable rest facilities for pregnant women or nursing mothers. The accompanying Approved Code of Practice (ACOP) suggests that such facilities should include provisions for lying down and should be near toilet facilities. This takes into account the physical and mental tiredness associated with pregnancy and the post-natal period, and the need for pregnant women to make frequent trips to the toilet as the growing foetus exerts increasing pressure against the mother's bladder.

In addition, the regulations require employers to protect non-smokers from the effects of tobacco smoke in rest areas/rooms. Given the known adverse effects smoking has on foetal development, this control of passive smoking is an important issue for pregnant women (further details of the effects of maternal smoking are discussed under *General Health Issues* section below). If rest areas, etc are shared by smokers and non-smokers, there should be sufficient and efficient extraction of the smoke from the area, although ideally there should be separate facilities for each. Some employers also offer health promotion schemes, which include assistance on giving up smoking, to their employees.

Q88. Are there any other welfare factors which must be considered?

A. There are no other legal requirements which relate to new or expectant mothers specifically. However, it is important for pregnant women to have ready access to toilet facilities as they have to make an increasing number of visits to the toilet as the pregnancy progresses. The provision of washing, changing and drinking water facilities are the same for new or expectant mothers as for any other employee.

Q89. Can new or expectant mothers work shifts?

A. Shift work is not suitable for everyone so the employer must ensure that employees working shifts are not suffering from any adverse effects which may result in physical or mental health problems — this applies to all employees working shifts not just new or expectant mothers.

There is no reason why pregnant women cannot work shifts in the early stages of their pregnancy, especially if they are used to the shift system in place. As the pregnancy proceeds the pregnant woman will become increasingly tired and shift work may start to cause adverse health effects. Employers should regularly assess shift work to ensure it is not having any detrimental effects on pregnant women.

If there are any indications of problems the pregnant women should be moved to work which involves more acceptable hours. The same is true for a new mother who may find it difficult to adjust to shift work after the birth of her baby and who may have problems resting herself and caring for her baby during the day if she works night shifts.

Under the **Management of Health and Safety at Work (Amendment) Regulations 1994** (SI 1994 No. 2865), employers are obliged to alter a new or expectant mother's working hours if doing so would avoid an identified risk. Suspension from work, including night work, may also be considered.

Q90. Do some shift patterns represent a greater risk than others?

A. The human body works to a defined biological (circadian) cycle which follows the pattern of activity during the day and sleep/rest at night. Where work shifts interfere with this natural cycle there may be some adverse effects on health. The ability to cope with the disruption varies between individuals — some will be able to adapt, some will not and their suitability for shift work must therefore be assessed.

Workers who work the same shift patterns all the time will probably adjust to changes in their body cycle and will become used to working at night and resting during the day. Where workers work different shift patterns on a rota basis, they will find it more difficult to adjust as they will have to continually change between working nights and days.

The effects can be reduced by allowing a long rest period, eg three or four days, between each rota change. These shifts tend to be more significant from a health and safety point of view. Apart from the effects of increasing tiredness which are likely to affect a new or expectant mother's ability to do shift work regardless of the shift pattern involved, there is no evidence that they are at any greater risk than other employees.

Q91. Can new or expectant mothers work a normal length day?

A. Yes. There is no reason why new or expectant mothers cannot work their normal hours provided there is no evidence that those hours are having an adverse effect on their health. The **Management of Health and Safety at Work (Amendment) Regulations 1994** (SI 1994 No. 2865) require employers to alter the working conditions and/or the working hours of new or expectant mothers where this would avoid an identified risk to their health and safety. Changes that may be considered include a shorter working day and/or flexitime, both of which would allow the new or expectant more flexibility in her time at work and allow her to travel outside of the rush hour period.

Q92. Are new or expectant mothers entitled to additional breaks from their work?

A.   There is no specific statutory entitlement for new or expectant mothers to take extra breaks away from their work, although the **Management of Health and Safety at Work (Amendment) Regulations 1994** (SI 1994 No. 2865) do require employers to alter the working conditions of a new or expectant mother if doing so would avoid an identified risk to her health and safety, ie increasing tiredness and fatigue.

This could include provision for additional rest breaks, eg women in late pregnancy and new mothers may need a rest period after lunch. More frequent rest breaks may also need to be considered if the new or expectant mother cannot sit down during her work, has to spend long periods in one position or is working in extreme conditions, eg very hot or cold environments, etc, although in this latter case the need for additional breaks would apply to all workers in those areas, and not just to new or expectant mothers.

Q93. Are new or expectant mothers at particular risk from operating machinery?

A.   New or expectant mothers are not necessarily more at risk than other workers when operating machinery. However, there are several factors which employers should take into consideration when assessing and reviewing such risks in relation to new or expectant mothers.

First, the metabolic changes which occur during pregnancy can reduce mental concentration which may increase the risk not only to the new or expectant mother, but also to any one else working directly with, or near, her. Second, the increasing size during pregnancy may affect a pregnant woman's ability to achieve or maintain the correct operating position for the machine, which in turn may reduce her level of control over it. Third, manual dexterity, co-ordination and mobility can be reduced which may affect how effectively the new or expectant mother can control a machine, especially in an emergency situation. Finally, pregnancy also increases the number of times that pregnant women have to go to the toilet, so it is important that a pregnant woman can leave her job easily as necessary.

The onus is on the employer to keep any relevant risk assessments under review so that any changes during the pregnancy and post-natal period which affect a new or expectant mother's ability to operate machines safely are addressed.

Q94. **Are slips, trips and falls significant hazards to new or expectant mothers?**

A.   Yes. Slips, trips and falls on the same level are the second most common type of accident to employees over all industries. Pregnant women are particularly vulnerable because of the change in the body s centre of gravity and increasing size as the foetus grows, which subsequently affects the pregnant woman's agility and balance. The large girth size in late pregnancy may also restrict downward vision, so items left on the floor or at low level cannot be seen and avoided.

Measures which can reduce these risks are to route wires away from walkways and access/egress points, etc, implement a 'clean up spillages immediately' policy, and instill in staff the need to shut all drawers which are not actually in use and to pick up any items which are left or dropped on the floor. Work activities where there is a high risk of slipping, tripping or falling, such as in swimming pool areas, or with work involving small children where toys may be left all around the floor, will need to be kept under review so that any risk does not become unacceptable.

Q95. **Are new or expectant mothers at greater risk from work-related stress than other employees?**

A.   Vulnerability to stress is highly individual and within any workplace there will be workers who either can or cannot cope with pressure, whether work-generated or externally-related. There is no evidence that new or expectant mothers are particularly at risk, although there are several reasons why employers should keep the situation under review.

First, pregnancy causes physiological and hormonal changes to occur in a woman's body which in turn may cause psychological changes which could be exacerbated by work-related stress. Common causes of work-related stress include lack of control over the work, too much to do, too little to do, boring/repetitive work, etc. Where the changes which occur during pregnancy affect the woman s ability to have full control over her work, or reduce her speed and/or competence, eg work which occurs at a pre-determined rate, then stress factors may appear. Where stress causes a rise in blood pressure then a pregnant woman may be at increased risk of pre-eclampsia, a condition associated with high blood pressure which can have serious effects particularly in late pregnancy.

It is also fairly common for new mothers to suffer post-natal depression for some time after the birth of their child, and during this period it is also likely that they will be more susceptible to pressure at work and consequently stress.

It is important for employers to recognise the factors that may lead to stress so that appropriate control measures can be implemented. Similarly is is important to recognise when stress has arisen, so that this can be addressed. Many employers offer stress counselling facilities for employees suffering from stress-related problems. Even if the stress is not work-related it can cause a reduction in the employee's concentration and affect productivity, and may ultimately need the employer to intervene. It must, however, be recognised that prevention is better than cure, and treating stress is addressing the symptom and not the cause.

Q96. **Should new or expectant mothers be allowed to work in potentially violent situations?**

A.   Where there are identifiable risks of violence within the work undertaking these should be addressed in the risk assessment for all employees. It is reasonable to assume that pregnant women may be at increased risk because of the physiological changes which occur during pregnancy, ie proneness to fatigue, increasing girth size with consequent reduction in balance, mobility and agility, etc. They may therefore be less able to control or restrain any violent situation which arises, or ultimately to defend themselves. In this latter case there is a real risk of harm to the baby as well and this must be taken into account.

Employers should consider what is the policy for dealing with violent situations:

(a) are employees trained to recognise and handle violence, including methods of restraint?

(b) are employees required to always attend to violent situations in pairs, if so are there adequate staff resources?

(c) how fit and capable is the pregnant woman to deal with violent situations — can she protect herself and her colleagues?

Where a risk of violence is identified in relation to pregnant women they should be removed from exposure to such situations, if necessary by providing suitable alternative work, or ultimately by suspension.

Q97. **Are there any restrictions on new or expectant mothers travelling?**

A.   It depends on the particular mode of travel, and on the actual work activity, eg there may be different considerations for new or expectant mothers who are drivers as opposed to passengers.

For new or expectant mothers who are drivers the main areas for assessment will be the confined work space, especially for bus, coach or lorry drivers, etc; the potential for long periods of time in one position; a possible reduction in mental concentration and physical co-ordination, and the difficulty in maintaining ready access to toilet facilities and in taking breaks. The employers of new or expectant mothers who are required to drive a car for their work purposes, must assess and keep under review the woman's ability to perform her job without detriment to her health and safety. If the risk becomes unacceptable, then some control measures will have to be implemented. Individual vehicle operators will have their own policies and procedures for new and expectant mothers, and if there are any particular concerns then the woman's General Practitioner (with her written consent) or other professional medical advice should be sought.

For new or expectant mothers who are passengers there are again several considerations. Long distance travel is safer after the first 14 weeks of pregnancy when there is less risk of miscarriage. Many airlines impose restrictions on pregnant women travelling on international flights after 34 weeks of pregnancy, or on domestic flights after 36 weeks. Medical certification confirming the actual stage of the pregnancy may be required. Baggage handling and transfers may also cause a problem from a manual handling point of view.

If women in the late stages of pregnancy have to travel on aeroplanes, trains, coaches or buses then their employers would be well-advised to check with the individual operators for any travel restrictions in these circumstances, and if necessary seek professional medical advice.

Q98. **Do pregnant women have to wear road vehicle safety belts?**

A.   Yes. There is no legal exemption that allows pregnant women to travel in road vehicles without wearing safety belts. However, they may be exempt from wearing safety belts on medical grounds on the advice of an examining doctor, who must provide a written certificate confirming the exemption and the medical reasons.

The examining doctor may be the woman's General Practitioner (who may charge for the examination and certificate) or a doctor at one of the regional medical boarding centres, where the service is free for women on social benefits, which includes maternity pay.

However, if the pregnant woman is required to travel by her employer then the employer should pay for any such exemption certificates. Employers may also need to consider the situation regarding a new mother who may find safety belts uncomfortable to wear due to the increase in size and sensitivity of her breasts while breast feeding.

Q99. **Are there any special considerations for new or expectant mothers who have to work abroad?**

A. The degree of work-related risk to new or expectant mothers working abroad depends on several factors. The first factor is the actual country where the work is undertaken. Generally speaking, developed countries are lower risk than the third world countries, and are likely to have an established supporting infrastructure, such as reliable and accessible transport systems, health and safety enforcement procedures and medical facilities.

The second factor is the standard of health and safety management at the foreign place of work and the availability of corporate support for any new or expectant mothers, where this is needed. Local branches of some multinationals in some countries may not have or achieve the same level of health and safety standards that UK companies generally do.

The third factor is the mode of travel and the frequency of the trips. As discussed above there are various guidelines for pregnant women travelling by air. Finally, it may also be necessary for new or expectant mothers to have vaccines for the country where they are required to work, which may present problems through exposure to biological agents (see *biological agents* above). Medical advice should be sought.

One other effect of long distance travel where regular crossing of the time zones is encountered is that it can affect the menstrual cycle which may in turn affect the ability of a woman to conceive. Employers who require new or expectant mothers to travel abroad should get a medical opinion on the risks involved to new or expectant mothers, and should as far as possible ensure acceptable control measures and support services are provided once the new or expectant mother arrives.

Good communication systems will be important. Contingency plans should be in place in case of medical problems, such as premature birth or miscarriage, etc in order to get the woman home quickly. New or expectant mothers should be provided with training, information and instruction on the risks they are likely to encounter and the appropriate ways to respond.

Q100. Are there any special insurance provisions which apply to the employment of new or expectant mothers?

A.   No. All employers are required to have employers' liability insurance which is intended to cover them against claims from employees for personal injury sustained at work. This covers all employees including new or expectant mothers. There is no requirement for employers to notify their insurers that they have new or expectant mothers at work. The only influence an insurance company may have is in situations where there were identified risks to new or expectant mothers which the employer failed to control. If these result in claims for personal injury damages, then the insurance company may increase the employer's future liability insurance premiums, or in extreme cases may refuse to offer further insurance cover (note that employers may not legally operate without employer's liability insurance). In fact many insurance companies do take the effectiveness of health and safety management within a company into consideration when calculating the premiums payable.

Q101. Are members of the public who are new or expectant mothers covered by any special insurance?

A.   In workplaces where the public are invited in, employers should have public liability insurance to cover any injuries sustained to members of the public while on their premises. As with employers liability insurance there are no special provisions for new or expectant mothers and where there are identified risks to such women then the employers should take appropriate measures to control them.

Q102. Are new or expectant mothers who work on a temporary or casual basis protected by health and safety law?

A.   Yes. Section 3 of the **Health and Safety at Work Act 1974** requires employers to ensure the health and safety of persons who are not the employer's employees but who may be affected by the employer's undertaking. This includes contractors, self-employed persons, temporary/casual staff, delivery personnel and visitors, etc. As with employees, a greater duty of care is owed to individuals who may be at increased risk, eg new or expectant mothers.

In addition, the **Management of Health and Safety at Work Regulations 1992** (SI 1992 No. 2051) require employers to provide relevant health and safety information to any temporary staff before they start work. If the temporary staff are supplied from an agency, then the employer must provide any relevant information to that agency, which is in turn required to pass it on to all of its staff working at the employer's undertaking. The information should include details of any risks associated with the workplace and the measures necessary to control those risks.

SUMMARY

In many cases new or expectant mothers will not be at any greater risk at work than other employees. However, where such risks are identified then the employer must take appropriate control measures to address them. Specific areas where employers may have to consider the risks to new or expectant mothers are: exposure to physical, biological and chemical agents; manual handling; suitability of emergency procedures, evacuation and access/egress routes; display screen work; the work environment; the provision of welfare facilities, stress; violence; hours of work (including shift work); and travelling abroad.

If any identified risks are properly controlled then there is no reason why new or expectant mothers should not be able to work normally until their confinement time.

EMPLOYMENT ISSUES

INTRODUCTION

Apart from the more obvious health and safety issues discussed above there are also several important employment law issues which should be included in relation to new or expectant mothers. While these may not be specific health and safety considerations, they may have health and safety implications, and/or are necessary for the sake of completeness. This chapter will look at relevant employment law legislation, maternity rights, protection against dismissal on maternity grounds, discrimination and the provision of support facilities, such as nursery or child care places.

Q103. What is the main legislation governing the employment rights of new or expectant mothers?

A.   After several recent changes in employment law the **Employment Rights Act 1996** has consolidated all the main previous require-ments. Ante-natal care is covered by ss. 55–57; suspension on maternity grounds is covered by ss. 66–68; maternity leave is covered by ss. 71–78; right to return to work after maternity leave is covered by ss. 79–85; dismissal, fairness and redundancy in relation to pregnancy and maternity are covered by ss. 96, 99, 137 respectively.

Q104. Can a pregnant woman work right up to her period of confine-ment?

A.   Yes. There is nothing in law to prevent a pregnant woman who is able to work without detriment to her own, or her foetus's health and safety, working through into the late stages of her pregnancy. The previous restriction which prevented women working beyond the final six weeks of their pregnancy has now been removed. The same applies to self-employed pregnant women, although the onus is on them to ensure their own health and safety and that of their baby.

In both cases medical advice should be considered if there are any concerns, or if the woman intends to work right to the end of her pregnancy. It is worth remembering that children born with any deformities or disabilities which were the direct result of some person's negligence may sue the negligent person for damages.

Q105. If an employer requests medical confirmation that a pregnant woman is fit to continue working late into her pregnancy, can this be construed as sex discrimination?

A. This is a very difficult subject and certainly any employer requesting such confirmation should have valid and justifiable concerns about the woman's well being if she continues at work. Even if medical confirmation is provided that a pregnant woman is fit to continue working, the employer must still assess and review the risks to her health and safety while she is at work. Paid time off should be given for the pregnant woman to attend the medical examination, etc, and there should not be any other detriment to her terms or conditions of employment. The ethic of medical confidentiality should also be maintained (see *General Health Issues* section below for details of medical confidentiality).

Employers are advised to consider and compare what action they would take if they were asking for medical information in relation to a male employee continuing work after an illness or injury in order to avoid unnecessary sex discrimination. Any such request for medical information made purely because the woman was pregnant could be interpreted as sex discrimination.

Q106. What is the current period of maternity leave?

A. The total period of maternity leave is a minimum of at least 14 weeks. However, women who meet the qualifying condition of two years continual service when their maternity leave is due to start, ie 11 weeks before the expected birth, are entitled to an extended maternity leave period of up to a further 29 weeks *from* the birth of their baby.

Q107. **Do employers have to maintain the new or expectant mother's contractual rights for the whole period of her maternity leave?**

A.   Yes. Employers must honour any contractual rights, such as holiday entitlement, etc of new or expectant mothers for the basic 14 week maternity leave period. The exception is remuneration which is likely to be limited to the woman's basic wage or salary rate as her wages or salary will be replaced by 'statutory maternity pay' (SMP) or 'maternity allowance' (MA) while she is on maternity leave. Women entitled to extended maternity leave will have their contractual rights protected for the first 14 weeks — what happens for the remainder of that leave period depends on their employment contracts.

Q108. **Are there any qualifying periods of service or hours of work which must be satisfied by new or expectant mothers before they are entitled to maternity leave?**

A.   No. Maternity leave of at least 14 weeks' duration must be given to all pregnant women regardless of their length of service or actual hours of work. This means pregnant women who work part-time or on a temporary basis have the same right to maternity leave as full-time employees. However, women who have had at least two years' continual service before starting maternity leave are entitled to an extended maternity leave of 29 weeks (from the birth of the baby).

Q109. **How much notice do new or expectant mothers have to give employers of the fact that they are pregnant and intend to go on maternity leave?**

A.   The pregnant woman must inform her employer in writing that she is pregnant, the expected week of the birth and the date she intends to start her maternity leave. This period must not be less than 21 days before she actually starts her maternity leave. The employer is entitled to request a medical certificate confirming the pregnancy and this confirmation must be received by the third week of the maternity leave in order to ensure statutory maternity pay is paid.

Pregnant women who are entitled to the extended period of maternity leave must also inform their employer that they intend to exercise their right to return to work.

Q110. Are there any restrictions as to when maternity leave can start?

A. Yes. Maternity leave normally starts after week 29 of the pregnancy, ie 11 weeks before the expected birth date. The women can, however, elect to continue working right up until the time of birth, if she is fit to do so. Unless a risk assessment indicates that this is not acceptable, she is entitled to carry on working. If there are medical reasons *associated with* the pregnancy which require the pregnant woman to be away from work within the last six weeks before the expected birth date, the woman's maternity leave would normally start with that absence, although she may negotiate with her employer to continue working until her intended maternity leave date, if the illness only lasts for a short time (no minimum period of absence is defined). In this latter situation the woman would be well-advised to obtain written confirmation of the arrangements from her employer.

In the case of babies being born before their expected birth date, the maternity leave starts on the date of the birth — the employer must be notified.

Q111. Can new mothers return to work immediately after the birth of their baby?

A. No. The **Maternity (Compulsory Leave) Regulations 1994** (SI 1994 No. 2479) prohibit any woman returning to work within two weeks of the birth of her baby. Similarly, s. 205 of the **Public Health Act 1936** prohibits women who work in factories from returning to work within four weeks of the birth of their babies.

Q112. When does the maternity leave period end?

A. Maternity leave ends either at the end of the 14 week period, or at the end of 29 weeks after the birth of the baby (for women entitled to the extended maternity leave period). For women entitled to the

14 weeks maternity leave who start their leave 11 weeks before the expected birth date, and who have a delayed birth which takes them over their 14 week entitlement, then their maternity leave is automatically extended to cover this. Under the **Maternity (Compulsory Leave) Regulations 1994** (SI 1994 No. 2479) no woman may return to work within two weeks of the birth of her baby — this provides additional protection to women who have delayed births and who would otherwise have to return to work immediately. Women entitled to extended maternity leave may defer their return to work for up to four weeks if they are ill — a medical certificate must be given to the employer. The employer is also entitled to defer the woman's return to work from extended maternity leave for up to four weeks, for any reason.

Q113. What notice period is a new mother required to give her employer of her intention to return to work?

A.   A new mother wishing to return to work before the end of her 14 week maternity leave must give her employer seven days' notice of her intention to return. This notice period is raised to 21 days for women returning to work after extended maternity leave. An employer is also permitted to write to a woman on extended maternity leave (after week 11 of the maternity leave) requesting confirmation of her intention to return to work — the woman must respond within 14 days.

Q114. What employment protection do new or expectant mothers have while they are pregnant or on maternity leave?

A.   It is considered 'unfair dismissal' for any woman to lose her job as a result of her pregnancy or her maternity leave. This applies regardless of the length of service or number of hours worked. Equally it is considered unfair for a pregnant woman or nursing mother to be selected for or made redundant because of her pregnancy or maternity, again regardless of length of service, etc. Suitable, appropriate alternative work must be offered to new or expectant mothers if it is available.

Sex discrimination is also a factor to be considered; employers found to offer new or expectant mothers less favourable employment terms, conditions, opportunities, etc because of the fact that they are pregnant or are nursing babies, will almost certainly be held to be guilty of sex discrimination.

Q115. Are new mothers returning from maternity leave entitled to have their old jobs back?

A. A woman returning from the basic 14 week maternity leave, is entitled to return to work to exactly her same job, and providing she does not intend to return early she is under no obligation to notify her employer. A woman returning from extended maternity leave has the right to return to work, but not necessarily to exactly the same job, although there must not be any detriment to her terms and conditions of employment if she is given another job.

Q116. Are employers obliged to give pregnant women time off for ante-natal care?

A. Yes. Employers cannot unreasonably refuse a pregnant woman paid time off work for ante-natal care purposes — this applies regardless of the length of service or number of hours worked. Ante-natal care is taken to include exercise and relaxation classes. The employer is entitled to ask for confirmation of the pregnancy and evidence of the second and subsequent ante-natal appointments. The time off allowed should include travelling and waiting time as well as the actual appointment.

Q117. Is there any course of redress for new or expectant mothers whose employers do not fulfil their obligations?

A. Yes. New or expectant mothers whose employers have failed to fulfil one or more of their duties are entitled to lodge a complaint with an Industrial Tribunal.

Q118. Are employers obliged to provide nursery facilities or child care facilities?

A.   No. There is no legal requirement for employers to offer nursery or child care facilities to their staff, although many employers now provide these services, in recognition of the value of retaining their staff. Where workplace nurseries are provided, these are not regarded as a taxable benefit by the Inland Revenue, and can therefore be economically advantageous to the mother.

SUMMARY

Although not mainstream health and safety issues, it is important to include basic information on the rights, etc of new or expectant mothers in employment law. The principle legislation on employment matters is the **Employment Rights Act 1996** which consolidates the previous aspects of employment law, including maternity rights and protection.

Employers have certain obligations such as allowing reasonable time off for pregnant women to attend ante-natal care appointments; provision of basic 14 week maternity leave, which in some circumstances is extended to 29 weeks, and protection of the employment of new or expectant mothers against sex discrimination, dismissal or redundancy actions. There are also a series of notifications which must be made between the employer and the new or expectant mother before certain duties or entitlements come into effect.

GENERAL HEALTH ISSUES

INTRODUCTION

This chapter looks at some of the more common health issues of relevance to new or expectant mothers. Again they are not specifically related to health and safety at work although they may be issues which employers will have to deal with at some time. The concerns discussed include smoking, alcohol, drugs, HIV/AIDS, allergies, pre-existing health conditions and medical confidentiality.

Q119. What are the dangers of exposure to tobacco smoke on new or expectant mothers?

A.   Women who smoke tend to have smaller babies than non-smoking mothers, and there is an increased risk of premature birth and perinatal death, ie death immediately before or after the birth. The onset of the menopause is often brought forward in women who are heavy smokers, and there is a significant increase in the risk of a smoking mother suffering a subarachnoid haemorrhage (bleeding on the brain). The incidence of pre-eclampsia (a serious condition in later pregnancy most commonly identified by high blood pressure and fluid retention in the body tissues) is lower in smokers — although if it does occur the effects are usually more severe. There is also an increased risk of congenital abnormalities such as heart defects and cleft palate in the baby of a mother who smokes.

Although employers do not have any control over the social habits of their employees many do now operate no smoking policies in their workplaces due to concerns about passive smoking and the possible liability under s. 2 of the **Health and Safety at Work Act 1974**, ie failing to ensure the health and safety of employees at work, or through the civil courts. In a lot of cases A smoking ban at work is supported by company-funded health promotion awareness schemes to help smokers give up.

Q120. What effects do drugs and alcohol have on new or expectant mothers?

A. Alcohol is known to cause abnormalities in babies such as small heads, mental impairment and deformities of the face, joints and sex organs. These are symptoms of a condition called foetal alcohol syndrome which is caused by maternal intake of excess alcohol. Many drugs have similar effects and can lead to addiction and withdrawal problems in babies born to mothers who take drugs. The term 'drug' is used in its widest form and includes not only illegal drugs, but also generally available and prescription medicines. In these latter cases the information which accompanies the medicine should be read carefully and if there is any doubt the pharmacist or the woman's General Practitioner should be consulted.

The effects of alcohol and drugs may be passed through the mother's milk to breast fed babies. Any temporary abstinence from these substances should include the post-natal and breast feeding periods. As with smoking above, many employers are introducing 'substance abuse' policies into their workplaces in order to eliminate, or at least reduce such consumption on site for obvious health and safety reasons. Again there may be health promotion awareness and counselling schemes supporting such policies to help employees give up. No form of medicine, including headache pills, should be kept in any workplace first-aid kit.

Q121. Can foetuses and babies contract the human immunodeficiency virus (HIV) from their mothers?

A. Yes. There are documented cases of babies of HIV-positive mothers carrying the HIV virus themselves. The virus can spread in three ways, ie across the placenta, through contact with the mother's blood during the actual birth, and through the mother's milk. Employers of new or expectant mothers who work in higher-risk occupations with regard to HIV, should ensure such women are aware of any HIV/AIDS policy and the associated risks and control measures.

Note: there is no obligation for an employee to inform their employer if they are HIV positive or have AIDS. If this information is volunteered, confidentiality must be maintained *at all times* unless the person consents otherwise.

Q122. Can mothers pass allergies on to their babies?

A. There is some evidence which suggests that it is possible for babies to be born with the same allergies as the mother. Most recently this has been suggested with nut allergies, where mothers with an allergy to nuts have given birth to babies who have the same allergy. From an employment point of view exposure to any substance which triggers an allergic response must be avoided, either by appropriate engineering controls, alternative work, or personal protective equipment — this applies equally to all employees not just new or expectant mothers.

Q123. Do employers have a right to request medical information which relates to any of their employees who are new or expectant mothers?

A. Yes. Employers may contact the General Practitioner of any employee, including new or expectant mothers, for medical information, *but only* with the consent of that employee. Even if the employer arranges and pays for a medical examination to ascertain certain medical facts about an individual, that medical information is confidential and may not automatically be provided to the employer without the individual's consent. However, the provision of information to the employer is important if the employer is to take all the necessary control measures to protect new or expectant mothers and their foetuses or babies. Employers cannot be held liable for any risks that they could not reasonably be aware of. To a certain extent, pre-employment health screening and interviews will help identify some problems in potential employees, although again this information is confidential and the employer may not necessarily be provided with exact details, just whether someone is fit/unfit to undertake a particular post. Conversely, it is equally important for the General Practitioners of new or expectant mothers to be informed of the nature of the woman's work and of any specific risks so that appropriate medical advice can be offered.

Q124. Can employers request new or expectant mothers to undergo a medical at any time in their employment?

A.　　Generally yes, although there must be valid reasons for the request, such as significant changes to the workplace or work activities, etc, or if there is a change in the new or expectant mother's health or if this is required by legislation (eg medical surveillance under the COSHH Regulations). The right of the employer to request employees to undergo medical examinations at any time in their employment should be included in the terms and conditions of the employees' contract.

Q125. Are new or expectant mothers allowed access to the report of any medical examination they are required to undergo at work?

A.　　Yes. Under the **Access to Medical Reports Act 1988**, persons, including new or expectant mothers, who undergo a medical examination, have a right to see the subsequent report within 21 days of the date that the application for the medical report was made by the employer. During this time the employer is not allowed to see the report. The person to whom the report relates may object to certain points and request the doctor to amend them. If the doctor refuses to carry out such amendments the person may submit a statement with the report to clarify/explain any of the contents they are unhappy with. The doctor is entitled to keep parts, or all, of the report from the person it relates to if the doctor feels that the disclosure of such information may seriously physically or mentally harm that person.

　　　If an individual exercises their right to see the medical report before it is submitted to the employer, they must again give their consent before the report can be passed on.

Q126. What is the correct procedure for employers to follow if they require medical information about a new or expectant mother?

A. There must be justifiable reasons for requesting the information and these should be discussed with the new or expectant mother initially. The new or expectant mother should be made aware of her rights under the **Access to Medical Reports Act 1988**, which in summary include:
   - the right to withhold consent for the employer to request medical information from a doctor
   - the right to see the report before it is sent to the employer
   - the right to request amendments to the report, or where this is refused by the doctor, to add a personal statement
   - the right to withhold consent for the report to be sent to the employer.

Her permission must then be given, in writing, for the employer to *approach* a doctor for the medical information, and then for the medical details to be *disclosed* to the employer. An example of the appropriate consent forms, and explanatory note on the rights of individuals under the **Access to Medical Reports Act 1988** are given as *Appendix A* after the end of this chapter.

Q127. Is there any statutory requirement governing the issues of confidentiality?

A. No. There is no law which requires confidentiality to be maintained, so in most cases, the issue of confidentiality is covered by relevant codes of professional practice. However, if confidentiality is broken then the person aggrieved by that action may sue for the alleged breach of the confidentiality they were owed, through the civil courts.

Q128. Are there any times when confidentiality can be broken?

A. Yes. Confidentiality may be broken by doctors and nurses in four clearly defined and serious circumstances:
   (a) if the individual is at grave risk
   (b) if the community is at grave risk

(c)   if the doctors/nurses are at grave risk

(d)   in the event of other exceptional circumstances, which must be justifiable.

Q129.   What examples are there of pre-existing health problems which may be significant in the case of new or expectant mothers?

A.   Examples of health conditions which may be relevant to new or expectant mothers at work are diabetes, heart disease, high blood pressure and thromboembolism (blockage of a blood vessel caused by a detached fragment of an existing blood clot from elsewhere in the body). If employers are aware of any pre-existing health conditions, then they would be well-advised to get medical advice about whether a new or expectant mother suffering from any of these conditions should be working, or requires any special considerations such as extra rest breaks, breaks at regular and predetermined times, etc.

SUMMARY

Although employers cannot be responsible for lifestyles and events which occur outside of the workplace, there is an onus on them to be aware of external factors which may be made worse through the work undertaken by a new or expectant mother. This situation is complicated by the ethics of confidentiality which must be observed at all times. It also requires employers to have valid and justifiable reasons for requiring additional medical information on an employee who is a new or expectant mother, and controls what happens to that information once it is received.

It is well-known that smoking, substance abuse, HIV, and the presence of pre-existing health conditions can all have an adverse effect on foetuses or new babies as well as on the mother. Employers must ensure that the new or expectant mother's work does not exacerbate any of these effects, as far as is possible.

APPENDIX A

EXAMPLES OF APPROPRIATE CONSENT FORMS AND ACCOMPANYING NOTES FOR THE PROVISION OF MEDICAL INFORMATION

Form 1 → GP

The Children's Trust
TADWORTH

Employee Application For A Medical Report — Employee Consent Form

For reasons which have already been explained to you, The Children's Trust is seeking your consent to apply to a doctor for a report giving information about your state of health. You are not obliged to give your consent to such an application being made but any decision that The Children's Trust might have to take will then be taken on only those facts that are already available.

Before you sign in the space below, you should be aware that you have certain rights under the **Access to Medical Reports Act 1988**. In summary these rights are:

1. To withhold your consent for an application to be made to a doctor.
2. To see the medical report before it is supplied to The Children's Trust.
3. To ask the doctor to amend any part of the report which you consider to be inaccurate or misleading.
4. To attach a written statement giving your views on the contents of the report, if the doctor refuses to amend it (as above).
5. To withhold your consent to the report being supplied to The Children's Trust.

Note: the doctor may withhold from you sections of the report if he or she thinks you would be seriously harmed by seeing it.

The attached note sets out in detail your rights under the 1988 Act and the procedures for applying them. Please read the whole of the attached note before signing below.

If you have any questions concerning the contents of the form please contact the Occupational Health Department.

....

1. I have been informed of my statutory rights under the **Access to Medical Reports Act 1988** and hereby give my consent for The Children's Trust to apply for a report giving medical information from a doctor who has been responsible for my physical or mental health care.

   I understand that this consent form will be copied to that doctor and shall have the validity of the original.

2. I do/do not* wish to see the medical report before it is sent to The Children's Trust.

* Please delete as appropriate

Signed : .... Date: ....

Form 2 → **Employee**

The Children's Trust
TADWORTH

Explanatory Note For Employees — Access To Medical Reports Act 1988

This note sets out your statutory rights under the **Access to Medical Reports Act 1988** and explains the procedure for applying these rights. Under the Act the employer cannot apply for a medical report from a doctor who has been responsible for your physical or mental health care without your consent. The consent form overleaf also asks, in accordance with the Act, whether you wish to see the report before it is sent to The Children's Trust.

If you have decided that you would like to see the report first, The Children's Trust will inform the doctor of that fact and will notify you of the date that the application for the medical report is actually made (Form 3). You will then have 21 days in which to make arrangements yourself for seeing the report — The Children's Trust cannot make them for you. Whilst there is no charge for reading the report, if you arrange with your doctor to have the report photocopied and, if necessary posted to you, the doctor may charge a reasonable fee to cover the cost of doing so.

If you did not indicate on the consent form that you wish to see the report but later change your mind, on your own initiative, you will be able to notify the doctor that you wish to see the report before it is sent to The Children's Trust. You will then have 21 days from the date of your notification to the doctor to make arrangements to see the report. Please note, however, that the doctor is not obliged to delay supplying the report to The Children's Trust in case you change your mind. By the time you have decided that you would rather see the report first, the doctor may already have supplied it to The Children's Trust.

If, following notification to the doctor, you have seen the report, the doctor will not be able to supply the report to The Children's Trust without your further consent. Having seen the report, you will be entitled to request that the doctor amend any part of the report which you consider to be inaccurate or misleading. If the doctor does not agree to amend the report as requested, you will be able to attach a written statement to the report giving your view on its contents.

Whether or not you decide to see the report before it is supplied to The Children's Trust, the doctor will be obliged to keep a copy of the report for at least six months after the date it was supplied to The Children's Trust, and you will be entitled to have access to that report.

Please note that the doctor is not obliged to let you see those parts of the medical report that he or she believes would be likely to cause serious harm to your physical or mental health or that of others, or which would reveal information about another person or the identity of a person who has supplied the doctor with information about your health unless that person also consents. In those circumstances the doctor will notify you and you will be limited to seeing any remaining parts of the report.

You would be advised to keep this explanatory note for further reference.

Form 3 → Employee after form 1 has gone to GP

Information For Employees — Notification of Application for a Medical Report

Recently you gave consent for The Children's Trust to make an application for a medical report to be made to a doctor who has been responsible for your physical or mental health care, and indicated that you wish to see the report before it is supplied to The Children's Trust. You will recall that attached to the consent form was an explanation of your rights under the **Access to Medical Reports Act 1988** and which you were advised to keep.

In accordance with the Act I am writing to inform you that an application for a medical report has now been made and to remind you that you will have 21 days from the date of that application in which to make arrangements to see that report before the doctor supplies it to The Children's Trust.

To enable a speedy consideration of your case it is in your interests to contact the doctor (name and address below) as soon as possible to make arrangements to see the report. Should you decide not to contact the doctor, he or she will supply it to The Children's Trust after the 21 day period has expired.

You will still, however, have six months to ask your doctor to see or have a copy of the report after it has been sent to The Children's Trust. You will of course have lost the right to append any written statement to that report giving your views on its contents

....

Name and address of the doctor to whom the application for a medical report was made:

Name : ....

Address : ....

....

....

Date application was made to the doctor: ....

RELEVANT GUIDANCE

Copies of Acts and Regulations discussed in the text are available from the Stationery Office (mail and telephone orders only), PO Box 276, London SW8 5DT. Telephone orders 0171-873 9090 / Fax orders 0171-873 8200. General enquiries telephone 0171-873 0011 / fax enquiries 0171-873 8463.

All the publications listed below are priced and available from HSE Books, PO Box 1999, Sudbury, Suffolk CO10 6FS. Telephone: 01787 881165 / Fax: 01787 313995, unless otherwise stated.

New and expectant mothers

HS(G) 122	New and expectant mothers at work — a guide for employers

Responsibilities and rights

L1	A guide to the Health and Safety at Work etc Act 1974
HSC2	The Act outlined (free)
HSC3	Health and Safety at Work etc Act 1974 — advice to employers (free)
HSC5	Health and Safety at Work etc Act 1974 — advice to employees (free)
L21	Management of Health and Safety at Work Regulations 1992: ACOP
HS(G)65	Successful health and safety management
IND(G)132L	5 steps to successful health and safety management (free)
L23	Manual handling: guidance on the Manual Handling Operations Regulations 1992
L24	Workplace health, safety and welfare — Workplace (Health, Safety and Welfare) Regulations 1992: ACOP

IND(G)170L   Workplace health, safety and welfare — a short guide to the 1992 Regulations (single copies free)

L5   General Control of Substances Hazardous to Health Regulations 1994: ACOP (includes ACOPs for hazardous substances, biological agents and carcinogens)

L25   Personal protective equipment: guidance on the Personal Protective Equipment at Work Regulations 1992

IND(G)174L   A short guide to the Personal Protective Equipment at Work Regulations 1992 (single copies free)

L26   Display screen equipment at work: guidance on the Health and Safety (Display Screen Equipment) Regulations 1992

IND(G)36L   Working with VDUs (single copies free)

HSE4   Short guide to the Employers' Liability (Compulsory Insurance) Act (free)

The following leaflets are available from local offices of the Department of Social Security.

Leaflet NI 253 Ill and unable to work

Leaflet IB 201 Incapacity benefit — a guide for people getting sickness benefit, invalidity benefit, severe disablement allowance, disability premium paid with income support, housing benefit or council tax benefit

Leaflet IB 202 Incapacity benefit — information for new customers

Leaflet IB 207 Introducing incapacity benefit.

Specific health and safety issues

HS(G)122   New and expectant mothers at work — a guide for employers

HS(G)137   Health risk management — a practical guide for managers in small and medium sized enterprises

IND(G)163L   5 steps to risk assessment (single copies free)

IND(G)213L	5 steps to information, instruction and training — meeting risk assessment requirements (free)
IND(G)218L	Guide to risk assessment requirements — common provisions in health and safety law (single copies free)
IND(G)226L	Homeworking — guidance for employers and employees on health safety (single copies free)
L23	Manual handling: guidance on the Manual Handling Operations Regulations 1992
IND(G)109L	Lighten the load — guidance for employers on musculoskeletal disorders (single copies free)
IND(G)110L	Lighten the load — guidance for employees on musculoskeletal disorders (single copies free)
IND(G)143L	Getting to grips with manual handling — a short guide for employers (single copies free)
IND(G)146P	Manual handling pocket card (single copies free)
L26	Display screen equipment at work: guidance on the Health and Safety (Display Screen Equipment) Regulations 1992
HS(G)90	VDUs — an easy guide to the Regulations
L5	General Control of Substances Hazardous to Health Regulations 1994: ACOP (includes ACOPs for hazardous substances, biological agents and carcinogens)
IND(G)136L	COSHH — the new brief guide for employers (single copies free)
HS(G)126	CHIP 2 for everyone
IND(G)181L	The complete idiots guide to CHIP 2 — a guide to the Chemicals (Hazard Information and Packaging Regulations 1994 (single copies free)
IND(G)182L	Why do I need a safety data sheet — for those who use or supply dangerous chemicals (single copies free)
IND(G)186L	Read the label — how to find out if chemicals are dangerous (single copies free)

L58	The protection of persons against ionising radiation arising from any work activity
IND(G)207	Wear your dosemeter pocket card (single copies free)
L24	Workplace health, safety and welfare — Workplace (Health, Safety and Welfare) Regulations 1992: ACOP
HS(G)132	How to deal with sick building syndrome
L22	Work equipment: guidance on the Provision and Use of Work Equipment Regulations 1992
HS(G)155	Slips and trips — guidance for employers on identifying hazards and controlling risks
IND(G)225L	Preventing slips, trips and falls at work (single copies free)
HS(G)116	Taking action on stress at work — a guide for employers
HS(G)133	Preventing violence to retail staff
IND(G)69L	Violence to staff (free)
COP42	First aid at work — Health and Safety (First Aid) Regulations 1981: ACOP

Employment issues

Reference book for employers Croner Publications Ltd, Croner House, London Road, Kingston upon Thames, Surrey KT2 6SR.

General health issues

IND(G)63L	Passive smoking at work (single copies free)
IND(G)62L	Protecting your health at work (single copies free)
IND(G)116L	What your doctor needs to know if you think you have a work related health problem (free)
NIS/18/01	Needlestick injuries (free)
IND(G)202L	Good health is good business — an introduction to managing health risks at work (free).

USEFUL ADDRESSES

Health and Safety Executive Information Line: 0541 545500

Health and Safety Executive (HSE) Area Offices

Employment Medical Advisory Service (EMAS) offices are located within the following HSE area offices.

SOUTH EAST

South East
3 East Grinstead House
London Road
EAST GRINSTEAD
West Sussex RH19 1RR
Tel: 01342 334200
Fax: 01342 334222

London N
Maritime House
1 Linton Road
BARKING IG11 8HF
Tel: 0181-235 8000
Fax: 0181-235 8001

London S
1 Long Lane
LONDON SE1 4PG
Tel: 0171-556 2100
Fax: 0171-556 2200

HOME COUNTIES

South
Priestly House
Priestly Road
BASINGSTOKE RG24 9NW
Tel: 01256 404000
Fax: 01256 404100

East Anglia

39 Baddow Road
CHELMSFORD CM2 0HL
Tel: 01245 706200
Fax: 01245 706222

Northern Home Counties

14 Cardiff Road
LUTON LU1 1PP
Tel: 01582 444200
Fax: 01582 444320

WEST AND WALES

South West

Inter City House
Victoria Street
Mitchell Lane
BRISTOL BS1 6AN
Tel: 0117-988 6000
Fax: 0117-926 2998

Wales

Brunel House
2 Fitzalan Road
CARDIFF CF2 1SH
Tel: 01222 263000
Fax: 01222 263120

Marches

Marches House
Midway
NEWCASTLE UNDER LYME ST5 1DT
Tel: 01782 602300
Fax: 01782 602400

MIDLANDS

East Midlands

5th Floor
Belgrave House
1 Greyfriars
NORTHAMPTON NN1 2BS
Tel: 01604 738300
Fax: 01604 738333

West Midlands

McLaren Building
2 Masshouse Circus
Queensway
BIRMINGHAM B4 7NP
Tel: 0121-607 6200
Fax: 0121-607 6349

North Midlands

Birkbeck House
Trinity Square
NOTTINGHAM NG1 4AX
Tel: 0115-971 2800
Fax: 0115-971 2802

NORTH WEST

Greater Manchester

Quay House
Quay Street
MANCHESTER M3 3JB
Tel: 0161-952 8200
Fax : 0161-952 8222

Merseyside

The Triad
Stanley Road
BOOTLE L20 3PG
Tel: 0151-479 2200
Fax: 0151-479 2201

North West

Victoria House
Ormskirk Road
PRESTON PR3 1HH
Tel: 01772 836200
Fax: 01772 836222

YORKSHIRE AND NORTH EAST

South Yorkshire

Sovereign House
110 Queens Street
SHEFFIELD S1 2ES
Tel: 0114-291 2300
Fax: 0114-291 2379

West and North Yorkshire	8 St Paul's Street LEEDS LS1 2LE Tel: 0113-283 4200 Fax: 0113-283 4296
North East	Arden House Regent Centre Regent Farm Road Gosforth NEWCASTLE UPON TYNE NE3 3JN Tel: 0191-202 6200 Fax: 0191-202 6300

SCOTLAND

Scotland East	Belford House 59 Belford Road EDINBURGH EH4 3UE Tel: 0131-247 2000 Fax: 0131-247 2121
Scotland West	West George Street GLASGOW G2 4LW Tel: 0141-275 3000 Fax: 0141-275 3100

INDEX